# Foreword

The examination of avalanche accidents contributes to safety education by drawing attention, in a dramatic way, to the snow conditions, the terrain, and the human actions that have caused injury, death and property damage. With this objective, the National Research Council of Canada, as the leading agency for avalanche research and information in Canada until 1991, compiled and published three volumes on avalanche accidents in Canada in 1979, 1980 and 1987. The Canadian Avalanche Association, as part of its mandate, now continues to promote avalanche safety and education by publishing this fourth volume.

The authors, Bruce Jamieson and Torsten Geldsetzer, have competently assembled the information and presented it in an unbiased, technical and instructive form. The National Search and Rescue Secretariat, recognizing the importance of prevention of snow avalanche accidents, has provided the primary funding for this publication. Even with the dedication of the authors and the financial support, this book could not have been written without the participation of the individuals, companies and government agencies who shared their knowledge. Their cooperation reflects the spirit of fellowship among avalanche technicians, ski and mountain guides, scientists and managers of avalanche safety programs in Canada, of which we can be proud. It is expected that this publication will further inspire them to work towards common goals, including the collection and sharing of data on significant avalanche events.

The four volumes of *Avalanche Accidents in Canada* show the advancement of expertise over the years. By scanning the four publications, one notices that the scenarios described in Volume 4 reflect better technical skills of all those involved than was the case 30 years ago.

A remarkable feature of Volume 4 is the thin section concerning industrial and transportation accidents; this topic filled one third of the pages of Volumes 1 and 2 (accidents between 1943 and 1978). This decrease of coverage is evidence of the growing awareness of avalanche hazards and the implementation of safety measures in industry. Similarly, the annual number of accidents in recreational activities has not increased substantially since 1978 despite the strong growth of skiing and snowmobiling in the backcountry. This is another proof of the success of education programs.

Although complete elimination of avalanche accidents may never be possible because a mountain snowpack is highly variable and avalanches often act in unpredictable ways, learning about the conditions that usually cause avalanches and being aware of avalanche hazards will continue to reduce the risks. This book is an excellent source of this type of instructive information.

Peter Schaerer

# Acknowledgements

The Canadian Avalanche Association is grateful to Canada's National Search and Rescue Secretariat's New Initiatives Fund and Canadian Heritage/Parks Canada for assisting in making the publication of this book possible, to Niko Weis for writing the proposal, to Alan Dennis for managing the project, to Diny Harrison for the drawings, to Peter Schaerer, Paul Anhorn, Chris Whalley and Torsten Geldsetzer for collecting the accident reports and summarizing them for the *Avalanche News*, to Mary Clayton, Laura Howatt and Lynn Freeland for compiling the data on non-fatal accidents, to Tony Daffern and Karl Klassen for advice on publishing, to Julie Lockhart for editing, to Jack Bennetto, Jon Bezzola, Alan Dennis, Clair Israelson, Peter Schaerer and Niko Weis for reviewing the manuscript, to Robyn Douglas and Gisela Geldsetzer for their support and patience, to Terry Reimer for the cover design and to Pat Morrow, Brad White and Terry Willis for the cover photos.

Also, this book would not be possible without the accident investigations, rescue reports and weather data submitted by:

Dave Aikens, Fernie Snow Valley Pro Patrol, Fernie, BC
Scott Aitken, BC Ministry of Transportation and Highways, Pemberton, BC
Bruce Allen, BC Ministry of Transportation and Highways, Revelstoke, BC
Greg Allen, Fernie, BC
Tim Auger, Banff National Park
Jim Bay, Revelstoke, BC
Tom Bell, BC Provincial Parks
Jack Bennetto, BC Ministry of Highways, Snow Avalanche Programs
Scott Berry, Calgary, Alberta
René Boiselle, Ste. Foy, Quebec
Gordon Burns, Cranbrook, BC
Canadian Avalanche Association InfoEx Subscribers
Canadian Mountain Holidays
John Clarke, Vancouver, BC
Ross Cloutier, Kamloops, BC
Crescent Spur Helicopter Skiing
Brian Cusack, Westcastle Ski Patrol
Eric Dafoe, Glacier National Park
Dale Davis, BC Coroners Service, Revelstoke, BC
Cristoph Dietzfelbinger, Smithers, BC
Environment Canada, Climate Services
George Evanoff, Prince George, BC
Alan Evenchick, BC Ministry of Transportation and Highways, Terrace, BC

George Field, Kananaskis Country, Alberta
Wayne Flann, Whistler, BC
Scott Flavelle, Squamish, BC
Lloyd Freese, Kluane National Park
Rod Gibbons, RK Helicopter Skiing
Kevin Giles, Nelson, BC
Bill Golley, BC Ministry of Transportation and Highways, Hope, BC
Paul Heikkila, BC Ministry of Transportation and Highways, Nelson, BC
Phil Hein, Golden, BC
Hemlock Valley Ski Area
Anton Horvath, Whistler Mountain
Clair Israelson, Parks Canada
Gerry Israelson, Jasper National Park
Rod Jaeger, Lac La Biche, Alberta
Bruce Kay, Blackcomb Ski Patrol
Brian Keefer, Field, BC
Kootenay Helicopter Skiing
Marc Lavallée, Ministry of Public Safety, Quebec
Marc Ledwidge, Banff National Park
Dave Liverman, Geological Survey, St. John's, Newfoundland
Hector MacKenzie, Whitehorse, Yukon
Bill Mark, Blackcomb Ski Patrol
Marmot Basin Ski Area
Bud Mercer, RCMP, Chilliwack
Mike Wiegele Helicopter Skiing
Nakiska Ski Patrol

Rod Pendlebury, Fernie, BC
Gord Peyto, Glacier National Park
Provincial Emergency Program, BC (PEP)
R.K. Helicopter Skiing
Royal Canadian Mounted Police (RCMP)
Peter Schaerer, North Vancouver, BC
Selkirk Tangiers Helicopter Skiing
Mark Shubin, Crawford Bay, BC
Kirstie Simpson, Whitehorse, Yukon
Alf Skrastins, University of Calgary
Rick Staley, Kluane National Park
Larry Stanier, Kananaskis Country

Chris Stethem, Chris Stethem and Associates
Tracey Telford, Salmo, BC
Roger Tierney, BC Parks, East Kootenay
    District
John Tweedy, BC Ministry of Transportation
    and Highways, Kootenay Pass
Art Twomey, Kimberly, BC
Tom Van Alstine, Nelson
Andy Vollmerhaus, Calgary, Alberta
Terry Willis, Yoho National Park
George Zilahi, North Shore Search and
    Rescue, Vancouver, BC

 Canadian Heritage    Patrimoine canadien
Parks Canada        Parcs Canada

Canadä

# Table of Contents

## Chapter 5 - Snowmobiling Accidents ...... 109

# Chapter 1

# Introduction

This is the fourth volume of *Avalanche Accidents in Canada*. Like its predecessors, this book reviews avalanche accidents in the hope that readers can use information from past accidents to avoid future ones. These volumes also strive to provide a reference so the facts of past accidents are not buried in filing cabinets and replaced by hearsay.

This book focuses on avalanche accidents between 1 October 1984 and 30 September 1996. It covers eleven *avalanche seasons* which are considered to run from October 1st—when snowfall in the mountains is likely to last the winter—until September 30th of the following year.

After this introduction, Chapter 2 presents basic statistics concerning avalanche accidents as trends and patterns. Chapter 3 by Scott Berry is a remarkable account of three backcountry skiers who all get caught in an avalanche and rescue themselves. The remaining chapters provide summaries of 87 avalanche accidents, broken down into skiing and snowboarding accidents (Chapter 4), snowmobiling accidents (Chapter 5), climbing and hiking accidents (Chapter 6) and avalanche accidents in industry, in buildings and on transportation routes (Chapter 7). Most of the accidents in these last four chapters involve fatalities. However, some non-fatal accidents are included because they illustrate points about avalanche terrain, mountain snowpack, rescue or readiness.

This summary of accidents is based on reports by organisations involved in public safety and rescue, commercial operations and recreationists. Avalanche investigators visit many fatal accidents and the resulting reports provide comprehensive information for preventing future accidents. However, many non-fatal accidents and are never reported; the experience and the wisdom gained is never shared. *Readers are strongly encouraged to report **all** avalanche accidents, including "near misses" and incidents that do not cause serious injury.*

Reporting of avalanche accidents:

- allows the Canadian Avalanche Centre to warn others about unexpected conditions through the Public Avalanche Bulletin and the Information Exchange,

- supports accident prevention programs of the Canadian Avalanche Association, national and provincial parks, and other agencies,

- supports the maintenance of search and rescue teams,

- focuses avalanche research on practical problems faced by recreationists, and

- is essential for educational books such as this one.

To facilitate reporting, the Canadian Avalanche Association provides a form which is included in Appendix A. The results may be included in graphs as in Chapter 2, or summarised individually as in Chapters 4-7. Names of those involved are not published, except with permission, as in Chapter 3.

Avalanche accidents in Canada share many characteristics with those in other countries. Approximately 150 fatalities (Schaerer, 1993) are reported per year by the 17 countries that are members of the International Commission for Alpine Rescue (ICAR). Eighty-five percent of these deaths occur in the Alps. However, many avalanche accidents also occur in countries such as Turkey, Russia and China that are not members of ICAR.

# Factors Contributing to Avalanche Accidents

## Trip Preparation

A trip plan can help recreationists avoid dangerous situations. By seeking information from maps, guidebooks, information centres and from people who have been in the area before, recreationists can plan alternate routes for poor weather and for unexpected avalanche

conditions. Also, members of the group should agree on the trip plan and objective before travelling to the trailhead.

Increasingly, snow stability information is available for more mountain areas of Western Canada as recorded telephone messages, posted notices at information centres or stores and over computer networks. In many of the accidents summarised in this book, backcountry users did not obtain this information before travelling into avalanche terrain.

Many avalanche victims and their parties are poorly prepared to search for a person buried by an avalanche. From October 1984 to September 1996, 75% of those that died as a result of non-commercial (recreational) avalanche accidents were not wearing avalanche transceivers! Probes, shovels and transceivers are all important for an efficient search by surviving members of the accident party. Apparently, some winter recreationists spend more money on their ski or snowmobile suits than on avalanche safety.

## Human Factors

Most backcountry travellers prefer to travel in informal groups without a designated leader. In such groups, decision-making may suffer. The people that migrate to the front of the group may be less skilled at assessing snow stability or at selecting routes in avalanche terrain than people further back. Also, people "back in the pack" may follow the track, paying little attention to the terrain or snowpack. The group should get together for important decisions about stability and the route. Sometimes a quiet voice asking, "But why do we think that slope is stable?" can prompt a careful re-assessment of the snow stability and ultimately, a sound decision. Also, involving less experienced people in route selection and stability assessment contributes to the experience of every person in the group, which will pay off in subsequent trips.

Fair weather can affect decisions. Blue sky draws recreationists towards open slopes and high passes. However, unstable snow can remain for days or sometimes weeks after the last storm. Decisions should be based on avalanche

bulletins, field observations and facts, and not on the good feeling of being out with friends on a blue sky day.

Many backcountry travellers are goal-oriented. Some get so focused on reaching a pass or a summit, that they continue even after learning of unfavourable conditions! We should be prepared to turn around and come back when the snowpack is more stable. Turning around can be difficult if the trip has been planned weeks ago, or if group members travelled a long way to get to the trailhead. However, the snow slopes will still be there next weekend, and next winter.

Some accidents happen late in the day, especially when the weather is poor. Under such conditions, backcountry travellers often become less careful about selecting routes or observing snowpack conditions (Fredston and others, 1995). Instead, they focus on getting "back to the barn."

If we find ourselves thinking, "It won't happen to me" or "It's probably okay to cross this slope," our safety margin is too thin. The snowpack continues to surprise even the most experienced people. We need a wide margin of safety so we can continue to enjoy the mountains, winter after winter.

## Terrain and Route Selection

While route selection is often a subtle art learned over many years, accidents show that some backcountry users do not know or choose to ignore the basics of terrain evaluation. Some enter gullies or large slopes capable of producing size 3 avalanches when they are aware that the snow is unstable. Others select slopes which—if they release—can carry them over cliffs or into trees, rocks, gullies or crevasses. Such terrain traps increase the risk of injury or deep burial, and decrease the chance of survival. Also, if the runout from a slide path is difficult for other members of the group to access, the risk to people crossing the path also increases.

## Safety Measures

Some safety measures, such as crossing possibly unstable slopes one-at-a-time or well-spaced out, reduce the likelihood of being caught by an avalanche. Other safety measures such as wearing transceivers or removing ski-pole straps tend to reduce the consequences of being caught. The accidents summarised in Chapters 4 to 7 illustrate that some winter recreationists do not know or do not practise such safety measures.

## Snowpack

In some accidents, people failed to recognise unstable snow conditions or heed the warning signs. These ranged from obvious indications such as recent fresh avalanches to thin hard-to-find weak layers in the snowpack. While most slab avalanches are released by weak layers of recently deposited snow crystals, most of the slabs that cause accidents are released by much older weak layers of faceted crystals or surface hoar. Such layers can remain sensitive to human triggering after being buried for weeks. Although occasionally misleading, field tests such as profiles and rutschblock tests are usually helpful in finding weak layers and assessing snow stability.

## Weather

Heavy snowfall, rain, drifting snow or warming—especially towards 0°C, are all signs of increasing avalanche danger. Some parties noted these signs but did not alter their route or plans to avoid or minimise the danger.

Also, poor visibility and "white-outs" make it difficult to keep the group together and select safe routes.

## Search and Rescue

Since about half of buried avalanche victims die within half an hour, the odds of finding a person alive are poor if the surviving members of the accident party go out to get help. Parties need to be equipped with transceivers, shovels and probes, and know how to use this equipment.

Trip preparation, recognizing avalanche terrain, assessing snow stability and backcountry search and rescue techniques reduce the chances of being caught in an avalanche and/or increase the odds of surviving an avalanche. The basics of these skills can be learned through avalanche awareness courses or by travelling with experienced people, and then refined over successive winters.

Appendix C contains a list of books on avalanche safety.

# Fatal Avalanche Accidents
# 1 October 1984 to 30 September 1996

| Date | Location | Fatalities |
|------|----------|-----------|
| 84-12-27 | Wawa Bowl, Banff National Park, Alberta | 1 out-of-bounds skier |
| 84-12-29 | Mt. Neptune, Rossland, BC | 2 helicopter skiers |
| 85-02-18 | Mt. Duffy, Monashee Mountains, BC | 2 helicopter skiers |
| 85-02-23 | Onion Mtn, Smithers, BC | 1 snowmobiler |
| 85-03-02 | Mt. Erris, Elkford, BC | 1 snowmobiler |
| 85-03-03 | Montagne Blanche, Quebec | 1 backcountry skier |
| 86-01-25 | White Queen Mountain, Nelson, BC | 1 backcountry skier |
| 86-02-04 | Selkirk Mountains, Nakusp, BC | 2 helicopter skiers |
| 86-02-07 | Crow Hill, Corner Brook, Newfoundland * | 1 tobogganer |
| 86-02-17 | Coquihalla Lakes, Cascade Mountains, BC | 1 backcountry skier |
| 86-03-29 | Clemina Creek, Monashee Mountains, BC | 4 snowmobilers |
| 87-03-23 | Thunder River, Cariboo Mountains, BC | 7 helicopter skiers |
| 87-05-29 | Bow Summit, Banff National Park, Alberta | 1 backcountry skier |
| 87-06-14 | Mt. Bryce, Banff National Park, Alberta | 3 climbers |
| 87-08-01 | Mt. Robson, Mt. Robson Provincial Park, BC | 1 climber |
| 88-01-17 | Standfast Creek, Selkirk Mountains, BC | 1 helicopter ski guide |
| 88-02-07 | Crowfoot Pass, Banff National Park, BC | 1 backcountry skier |
| 88-02-13 | Shawinigan, Quebec | 1 tobogganer |
| 88-02-20 | Fossil Mountain, Banff National Park, Alberta | 2 climbers |
| 88-03-22 | Sale Mountain, Selkirks, BC | 1 helicopter skier |
| 88-04-03 | Whitetooth Mountain, Golden, BC | 1 out-of-bounds skier |
| 88-12-28 | Extra Light, Yoho National Park, BC | 1 ice climber |
| 89-01-02 | Garibaldi Provincial Park, BC | 1 out-of-bounds skier |
| 89-01-04 | Middle Kootenay Pass, Pincher Creek, Alberta | 1 snowmobiler |
| 89-01-28 | Telegraph Creek, Coast Mountains, BC | 1 resident |
| 89-03-15 | Flute Mountain, Whistler, BC | 1 out-of-bounds skier |
| 89-03-15 | Bella Vista, Monashee Mountains, BC | 1 helicopter skier |
| 90-01-06 | Wawa Bowl, Banff National Park, Alberta | 1 out-of-bounds snowboarder |
| 90-01-28 | Sand Creek, Southern Rocky Mountains, BC | 1 snowcat skier |
| 90-01-30 | Battleship Mountain, Kokanee Glacier Prov. Park, BC | 2 backcountry skiers |
| 90-02-11 | Healy Creek, Banff National Park, Alberta | 4 backcountry skiers |
| 90-02-22 | Hartly Creek, Golden, BC | 1 ice climber |
| 91-01-20 | Rummel Col, Kananaskis Country, Alberta | 1 backcountry skier |
| 91-02-05 | Revier Malbaie, Quebec * | 1 tobogganer |
| 91-03-12 | Bugaboo Creek, Purcell Mountains, BC * | 9 helicopter skiers |
| 91-04-09 | Blackcomb Glacier, Coast Mountains, BC | 1 out-of-bounds skier |

# Fatal Avalanche Accidents, continued

| Date | Location | Fatalities |
|------|----------|------------|
| 91-11-27 | Twin Falls, Smithers, BC | 1 ice climber |
| 92-01-03 | Thornhill Mountain, Terrace, BC | 2 snowmobilers |
| 92-02-26 | Silk Tassel, Yoho National Park, BC | 1 ice climber |
| 92-04-22 | Mt. Dagon, Monarch Icefields, BC | 2 climbers |
| 92-12-13 | Owl's Head Mountain, Sicamous, BC | 1 snowmobiler |
| 92-12-19 | Mt. Strachan, West Vancouver, BC | 1 out-of-bounds skier |
| 92-12-25 | Parker's Ridge, Jasper National Park, Alberta | 1 backcountry skier |
| 93-02-18 | Tadousac Mountains, Quebec * | 1 hiker |
| 93-03-07 | Mt Skookum, Carcross, Yukon | 1 snowmobiler |
| 93-03-10 | Bourne Glacier, Revelstoke, BC | 1 snowmobiler |
| 93-03-17 | Bruins Pass, Glacier National Park, BC | 1 backcountry skier |
| 93-03-20 | Snow Dome, Jasper National Park, BC | 3 climbers |
| 93-05-24 | Hummingbird Ridge, Mt. Logan, Yukon | 1 climber |
| 93-08-09 | Mt. Temple, Banff National Park, Alberta | 1 climber |
| 93-11-28 | Mt. Howard Douglas, Banff National Park, Alberta | 1 backcountry skier |
| 94-01-05 | Oscar Creek, Ymir, BC | 1 snowmobiler |
| 94-02-13 | Hasler Creek, Chetwynd, BC | 1 snowmobiler |
| 94-02-13 | Middle Kootenay Pass, Pincher Creek, Alberta | 2 snowmobilers |
| 94-02-22 | Greely Creek, Selkirk Mountains, BC | 1 helicopter skier |
| 94-05-21 | Europa Lake, Coast Mountains, BC | 1 backcountry skier |
| 94-08-31 | Mt. Athabasca, Jasper National Park, Alberta * | 1 climber |
| 94-11-19 | Hemlock Valley Ski Area, Mission, BC | 1 ski patroller |
| 95-02-04 | Mt. Ryder, McBride, BC | 1 helicopter skier |
| 95-02-18 | Raven Lake, Cariboo Mountains, BC | 2 tobogganers |
| 95-02-19 | Burstall Pass, Kananaskis Country, Alberta | 1 backcountry skier |
| 95-02-24 | Cascade Mountain, Banff National Park, Alberta | 2 climbers |
| 95-02-26 | Bruce Creek, Purcell Mountains, BC | 1 snowmobiler |
| 95-03-05 | Broadview Mountain, Kakwa Recreation Area, BC | 1 snowmobiler |
| 95-03-10 | Blanc-Sablon, Quebec | 2 residents |
| 95-03-15 | Marmot Peak, Jasper National Park, Alberta | 1 out-of-bounds skier |
| 95-03-19 | Doctor Creek, Purcell Mountains, BC | 2 snowmobilers |
| 95-03-19 | Telkwa Range, Houston, BC | 1 snowmobiler |
| 95-11-12 | Sawtooth Mountain, Baffin Island, NWT | 1 snowmobiler |
| 95-12-22 | Robertson, Quebec | 2 backcountry skiers |
| 96-01-04 | No Name Ridge, Stagleap Provincial Park, BC | 1 snowboarder |
| 96-02-26 | Smugglers Ridge, Kokanee Glacier Prov. Park, BC | 1 backcountry skier |
| 96-03-26 | Mount Groulx, Quebec * | 1 backcountry skier |
| 96-05-17 | Mt. Cerebrus, Coast Mountains, BC | 3 climbers |
| 96-06-05 | Mt. Logan, Kluane National Park, Yukon | 1 climber |

* not summarised in Chapters 3-7 of current volume.

# Chapter 2

# Trends and Patterns in Avalanche Accidents

## Introduction

Throughout Canadian history, people, trains, automobiles, buildings and various other living and non-living things have been involved in avalanches. Trends and patterns in these avalanche accidents can be found in various forms and formats. For the purposes of this chapter we will start by looking at overall trends; then take a closer look at both recreational and industrial accidents; and finish off with an investigation into the survival factors of people caught in avalanches.

The statistics presented here draw on a database of all reported avalanche accidents between October 1, 1984 and September 30, 1996. During this period, 811 people were involved in 579 separate avalanches.

## Accident Trends

### Fatalities

The annual number of avalanche fatalities constitutes an important trend. During the time period covered in this book, 114 people lost their lives to avalanches. Looking at a longer period, 220 people in Canada have been killed by avalanches since 1970 (Fig. 2.1). Over this 26-year period there has been an average of 8.5 avalanche fatalities per year in Canada. During the past five years this average has increased to 10 fatalities per year. Today many more people are venturing into the mountains for recreation and therefore a corresponding increase in the number of fatalities could be expected. However, while the number of yearly fatalities has increased, on a per capita basis, the number of fatalities is actually going down. This lower proportion can hopefully be attributed to better avalanche information and public awareness.

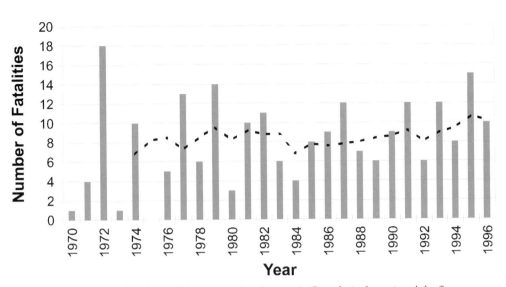

*Fig. 2.1  Number of avalanche fatalities per avalanche year in Canada (columns) and the five year run-ning average (dashed line). Total number of fatalities for the period is 220.*

## Age and Gender

Over the past 12 years, 90% of avalanche fatalities have been male. If we combine this statistic with the data from Fig. 2.2, we find that the typical avalanche victim is a man in his twenties.

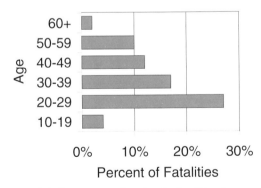

*Fig. 2.2  Percentage of avalanche fatalities by age for 72 fatalities (that reported age) between Octo-ber 1984 and September 1996.*

## Activities

In the first half of this century avalanche accidents happened primarily to people working in, or driving through, avalanche terrain.

Today avalanche accidents happen primarily to people during recreational pursuits. This change has come about through a number of factors. Better land zoning, workplace safety guidelines and highway control measures have dramatically decreased residential, industrial and transportation avalanche accidents. At the same time, many more people are travelling in avalanche terrain for recreation. As we can see in Table 2.1 and Fig. 2.3, most of those killed by avalanches are backcountry skiers, followed by snowmobilers, whose numbers have increased significantly in recent years.

## Recreational Accidents

Recreationists choose when to go into avalanche terrain. In doing so they have the potential to pick terrain appropriate to the weather and snowpack conditions. This section presents common factors in recreational avalanche accidents in hopes that this information will help recreationists select terrain that minimises the risks.

Both fatal and non-fatal accidents are used for most graphs in this section.

*Table 2.1  Number of fatalities by activity for a total of 220 fatalities.*

| Year | Skiers | Climbers | Snowmobilers | Other Recreation | Industrial/ Residential | Total Fatalities |
|------|--------|----------|--------------|------------------|-------------------------|------------------|
| 1978 |        | 5        |              | 1                |                         | 6                |
| 1979 | 12     | 1        | 1            |                  |                         | 14               |
| 1980 | 1      | 2        |              |                  |                         | 3                |
| 1981 | 8      | 2        |              |                  |                         | 10               |
| 1982 | 3      | 7        |              |                  | 1                       | 11               |
| 1983 | 2      | 3        |              |                  | 1                       | 6                |
| 1984 |        |          | 4            |                  |                         | 4                |
| 1985 | 6      |          | 2            |                  |                         | 8                |
| 1986 | 4      |          | 4            | 1                |                         | 9                |
| 1987 | 8      | 4        |              |                  |                         | 12               |
| 1988 | 4      | 2        |              | 1                |                         | 7                |
| 1989 | 3      | 1        | 1            |                  | 1                       | 6                |
| 1990 | 8      |          |              | 1                |                         | 9                |
| 1991 | 11     |          |              | 1                |                         | 12               |
| 1992 |        | 4        | 2            |                  |                         | 6                |
| 1993 | 3      | 5        | 3            | 1                |                         | 12               |
| 1994 | 3      | 1        | 4            |                  |                         | 8                |
| 1995 | 4      | 2        | 5            | 2                | 2                       | 15               |
| 1996 | 5      | 4        | 1            |                  |                         | 10               |

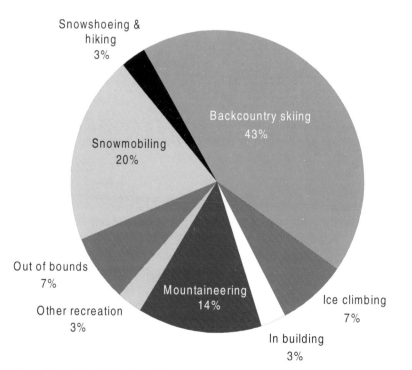

*Fig. 2.3  Canadian avalanche fatalities by activity for 114 fatalities between October 1984 and September 1996.*

## Month of Year

Between October 1984 and September 1996, 72% of recreational avalanche accidents occurred during the months of January, February and March (Fig. 2.4). An additional 12% occur during November, December and April bringing the total for the months of winter recreation to 84%. Sixteen percent of recreational avalanche accidents occur between May and October, indicating that avalanche danger can be a concern during the warmer months.

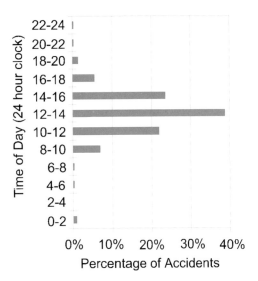

Fig. 2.5 *Percentage of accidents by time of day for 391 recreational accidents between October 1984 and September 1996.*

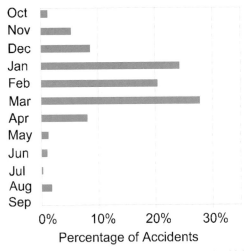

*Fig. 2.4 Percentage of accidents by month for 396 recreational accidents between October 1984 and September 1996.*

## Time of Day

Most recreational accidents occur during the daylight hours (Fig. 2.5). Between October 1984 and September 1996, 39% of accidents occurred between 12:00 and 14:00. Two factors may contribute to the peak in early afternoon:

- The number of recreationists in avalanche terrain (potential triggers and potential victims) probably reaches a maximum at this time.

- The air temperature usually reaches a peak between 12:00 and 14:00, and warming tends to reduce snow stability.

## Trigger

Avalanches that catch recreationists are usually triggered by members of the same party, whether they are on foot, on skis or on snowmobiles. In Fig. 2.6, only fatal accidents are considered because, in the period 1984-1996, few snowmobilers reported non-fatal accidents. Persons on foot or skis triggered 59% of the 58 fatal avalanches (with reported triggers) while those on snowmobiles triggered 24%. Cornices triggered 3% while 14%

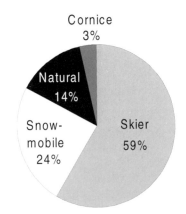

Fig. 2.6 *Percentage of fatal accidents by trigger for 58 recreational accidents (that reported the trigger) between October 1984 and September 1996.*

occurred naturally without cornice fall. This strongly indicates that the avalanches that catch, injure or kill recreationists are triggered by people. In fact, some of the avalanches reported as natural may have been triggered by people well below the fracture line who were uncertain if they had triggered it or not. This would have increased the percentage of human-triggered fatal avalanches to over 83%.

## Mountain Range

Between October 1984 and September 1996, 16% of the recreational accidents occurred in the Coast Mountains of BC, 39% occurred in the Interior Ranges of BC and 41% occurred in the Rocky Mountains (Fig. 2.7). Since winter recreation is more intense in the Interior Ranges than in the Rockies, more avalanche accidents might be expected in the Interior Ranges. However, the frequently shallow and unstable snowpack of the Rocky Mountains probably counters the effect of the less intense winter recreation.

During the 11 winters covered by this book, 72% of fatal accidents occurred in the triangle between Vancouver Island, Pincher Creek and Hinton, Alberta. Although this triangle represents a relatively small part of the mountainous areas in western Canada, the recreation in this area is intense.

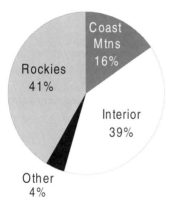

*Fig. 2.7 Percentage of accidents by mountain range for 380 recreational accidents between October 1984 and September 1996.*

The "other" category includes accidents in eastern Canada, mainly Quebec and Newfoundland. The accident involving residences at Blanc Sablon, Quebec on 10 March 1995 is an example. As a further indication of the seriousness of the avalanche problem in eastern Canada, 27 people in Newfoundland were killed in avalanches between 1863 and 1994 (Liverman, 1996).

## Treeline

The start zones of avalanches are classified as either alpine (above treeline), treeline or below treeline. The treeline is defined as the elevation band above the dense forests and below the area with very few or no trees. An important difference between these zones is wind exposure. Alpine areas are most exposed to the effect of wind on snowpack distribution. Treeline areas generally show less wind effect on snowpack distribution but the distribution is complicated by bands of trees that may act as snow fences. The effect of the wind on the snowpack is further reduced in dense forests below treeline.

Of the 396 recreational accidents between October 1984 and September 1996, only 80 reported whether the start zone was above, at, or below treeline. As shown in Fig. 2.8, 46% of these avalanches started in the alpine, 43% started at treeline and 11% started below treeline. At least three factors contribute to so many accidents occurring above the forests:

- Recreationists generally prefer areas without dense timber.

- The snowpack is generally more stable in dense forests than in areas with larger spacing between the trees.

- Wind action at and above treeline builds slabs in lee and cross-loaded areas. The resulting slabs are often less stable than the surrounding snowpack and can be difficult to recognise.

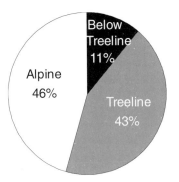

*Fig. 2.8 Percentage of accidents in relation to treeline for 80 recreational accidents between October 1984 and September 1996.*

Although only 11% of recreational accidents occurred below treeline, winter recreationists should also look for avalanche terrain and be prepared to assess snow stability when they are below treeline. In fact, one particular type of weak layer—buried surface hoar—is often more developed (larger crystals) and weaker in sheltered areas and logging cutblocks than in areas above treeline that are more exposed to the wind.

Forty-one of the alpine and treeline start zones were classified as either windward (facing the wind), lee (facing down-wind) or cross-loaded (facing parallel to the wind direction and allowing slabs to build in lee of the terrain features). Of these, 76% were lee slopes and 22%

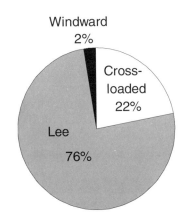

*Fig. 2.9 Percentage of accidents by wind exposure for 41 recreational accidents between October 1984 and September 1996.*

were cross-loaded (Fig. 2.9), highlighting the important interaction between terrain and wind in avalanche formation. Also, many recreationists seek the generally softer, deeper snow found on lee slopes. However, when travelling from one place to another through avalanche terrain, recreationists can improve their margin of safety by selecting windward slopes.

## Aspect

Avalanche accidents are not evenly distributed across the various slopes of mountains as shown in Fig. 2.10. This is likely a consequence of wind loading. The wind in western Canada often blows from the west, southwest or south depositing additional snow on east, northeast and north aspects. The resulting wind slabs tend to be unstable and recreationists are attracted to the often deeper snow on these aspects. Although these slopes are more often lee slopes than other aspects, wind deposits can be found on any aspect.

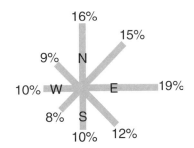

*Fig. 2.10 Percentage of accidents by aspect for 243 recreational accidents between October 1984 and September 1996.*

## Slope Angle

Dry slab avalanches rarely start on slopes of less than 25° and most recreational accidents involve dry slabs. The slope angle of the start zone was between 25° and 40° for 83% of the 184 recreational accidents that reported the slope angle (Fig. 2.11). Part of the reason many accidents occur between 25° and 40° is because many skiers, snowmobilers and snowboarders prefer to ski or ride slopes in this range. How-

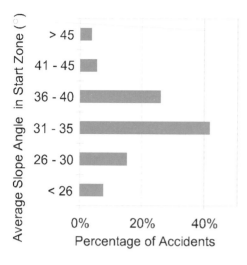

Fig. 2.11 Percentage of accidents by slope angle for 184 recreational accidents between October 1984 and September 1996.

ever, when the object is to get through avalanche terrain safely, recreationists can improve their margin of safety by not travelling on—or in the runout of—slopes of 25° or steeper.

## Terrain in Start Zone

The avalanches that cause accidents start more often at certain recognizable terrain features than at others. Terrain in the start zone may have more than one of the features shown in Fig. 2.12. For example, an avalanche that started at a convexity in a gully could be clas-

sified as either a convex slope or a gully, depending on which feature the reporter considered more important.

Fig. 2.12 shows the percentage of start zone features for 96 recreational accidents. Thirty-three percent of the start zones were classified as convex slopes, 12% as gullies and 22% as planar slopes. Twenty-three percent of the avalanches started at or near ridges and 10% started at rocks. Some avalanches are triggered at particularly weak snow that develops near large buried or exposed rocks.

It is usually not possible to avoid planar slopes, convex slopes and ridges without avoiding the avalanche terrain that many recreationists enjoy. Although route selection in avalanche terrain is a craft learned over many years, all recreationists can look for and consider these features when selecting routes. Certainly, convex slopes warrant extra caution when stability is in doubt.

## Ground Cover in Start Zone

The ground cover in the start zone plays a role in the stability of the overlying snowpack. For example, a deeper snowpack is required for avalanching over rough irregular ground than over relatively smooth ground involving rock, grass or small bushes.

As shown in Fig. 2.13, 46% of 90 accident avalanches started where the ground cover was rocky. Some of these may have been triggered from the particularly weak snow that can de-

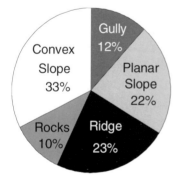

Fig. 2.12 Percentage of accidents by terrain feature in start zone for 96 recreational accidents between October 1984 and September 1996.

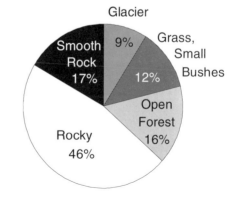

Fig. 2.13 Percentage of accidents by ground cover in start zone for 90 recreational accidents between October 1984 and September 1996.

velop near large buried or exposed rocks. Sixteen percent started in open forest but none started in dense forest. This may be partly due to the stabilizing effect of dense forest and partly due to the fact that many recreationists prefer open slopes to dense forests.

## Weather on Day of Accident

Weather has an effect on snow stability and on people. While stormy weather including precipitation, wind-loading and warming tends to decrease stability, recreationists more often seek out avalanche terrain under clear, cool conditions when winds are light.

Between October 1984 and September 1996, the sky conditions were reported for 79 recreational accidents. Fig. 2.14 shows the percentage of accidents for various sky conditions. Approximately half of the accidents (55%) occurred when the sky was overcast (100% cloud cover) or obscured (clouds not visible because of fog or snowfall). Alternatively, 45% of the accidents occurred when there was at least some blue sky, and 31% occurred when at least half of the sky was cloudless (scattered or clear).

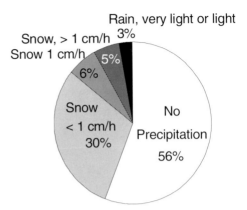

*Fig. 2.15 Percentage of accidents by precipitation for 110 recreational accidents between October 1984 and September 1996.*

at 1 or more cm per hour. During snowfall of less than 1 cm per hour, 30% of the accidents happened. Over 50% the accidents occurred when it was neither snowing nor raining. A total of 86% of the accidents happened when it was either snowing lightly or not precipitating. Obviously, it is under such conditions that recreationists (potential triggers and potential victims) often venture into avalanche terrain.

The wind speed at the time of 115 recreational accidents is shown in Fig. 2.16. In 72% of the accidents, the wind speed was either calm or light (< 26 km/h). The wind was only strong enough to cause drifting (moderate, strong or

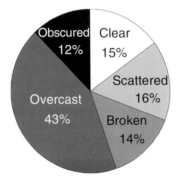

*Fig. 2.14 Percentage of accidents by cloud cover for 79 recreational accidents between October 1984 and September 1996.*

The precipitation at the time of 110 recreational accidents is shown in Fig. 2.15. None occurred during moderate or heavy rain probably since most mountain recreationists cancel their outings under such conditions. Only 3% occurred under very light or light rain. An additional 11% occurred when snow was falling

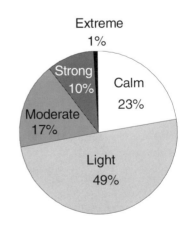

*Fig. 2.16 Percentage of accidents by wind speed for 115 recreational accidents between October 1984 and September 1996.*

extreme) in 27% of the accidents. Again, this shows that recreational accidents frequently happen under pleasant weather conditions.

Warming is generally believed to contribute to snow instability. However, when the percentage of recreational accidents is plotted against the temperature changes since the previous day, this effect is not apparent (Fig. 2.17). Temperatures had cooled since the previous day in 21% of the accidents and warmed in 13% of the accidents. The slight increase in accidents with cooling may be due to recreationists selecting avalanche terrain more often during the clearing and cooling that frequently follows a snowfall. Sixty-seven percent of the accidents happened when the temperature had increased or decreased by less than 2.5°C

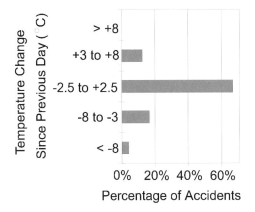

*Fig. 2.17 Percentage of accidents by temperature changes since previous day for 24 recreational accidents between October 1984 and September 1996.*

## Snowpack Factors

Recent snowfall generally contributes to instability by putting additional load on the weak layers in the snowpack. During the period of 1984 to 1996, the term *new snow* referred to snow that had fallen in the previous 12 or 24 hours. Fig. 2.18 shows that most recreational accidents happened when there had been less than 10 cm of new snow. This is not surprising since commonly less than 10 cm of

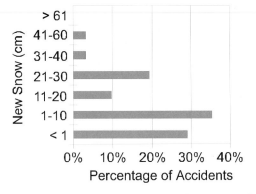

*Fig. 2.18 Percentage of accidents by amount of new snow for 31 recreational accidents between October 1984 and September 1996.*

snow falls per day. Although the new snow was only reported for 31 accidents, it is worth noting that the number of recreational accidents did not increase as the amount of new snow increased. Again, recreational accidents are associated with generally fair weather.

Storm snow is the height of snow that has accumulated and settled since the start of the last storm. Fig. 2.19, which is based on 42 accidents, shows no relationship between the height of storm snow and the percentage of avalanche accidents.

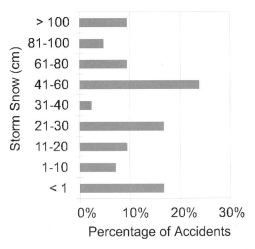

*Fig. 2.19 Percentage of accidents by the amount of storm snow for 42 recreational acci~~~~~een October 1984 and September 1996*

## Type of Avalanche

Avalanches start in one of two ways: either cohesive snow releases as a slab avalanche or relatively cohesionless snow releases as a loose avalanche (also called a point release avalanche). Both type of avalanches can be either dry, moist or wet. Fig. 2.20 shows the percentage of recreational accidents (from a total of 94) for the various types of avalanches. Slab avalanches accounted for 95% of all recreational accidents and most of these were dry slab avalanches. This is not surprising since most skiers, snowmobilers and snowboarders seek out dry snow conditions.

Sixty percent of the slab avalanches started as soft slabs and the remaining 40% started as hard slabs.

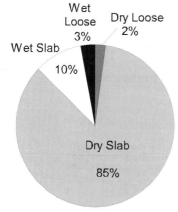

Fig. 2.20 *Percentage of accidents by type of avalanche for 94 recreational accidents between October 1984 and September 1996. Moist avalanches are included with wet avalanches.*

## Slab Thickness

The average slab thickness in the start zone was reported for 261 slab avalanches. Sixty-three percent of the slabs were less than 60 cm in thickness and 89% were less than 100 cm in thickness (Fig. 2.21). This corresponds to the range for which skiers, persons on foot and snowmobiles are efficient triggers. However, once triggered, thicker slabs tend to propagate ⌐urther, resulting in larger and more destruc-
 ⌐alanches.

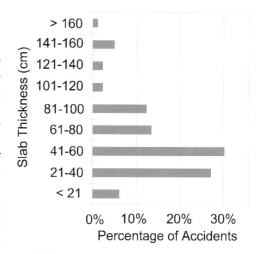

Fig. 2.21 *Percentage of accidents by slab thickness for 261 recreational accidents between October 1984 and September 1996.*

## Grain Structure of Failure Plane

Slab avalanches cause most recreational accidents and failures within weak layers at the base of the slabs (failure planes) are widely believed to initiate slab release. The grain structure of failure planes varies considerably. Some consist of crystals little changed from the time they fell (new snow forms or precipitation particles), while others consist of faceted crystals, depth hoar or surface hoar (frost) which do not fall from clouds but rather form on the surface or within the snowpack. These latter types can remain weak for a month or more and are called persistent weak layers.

In a study of fatal avalanches in Canada between 1972 and 1991, Jamieson and Johnston (1992) found that the failure planes for 68% of fatal slab avalanches consisted of persistent grain types (facets, depth hoar and surface hoar). There are several reasons for this:

- Since the persistent weak layers remain weak longer, they remain sensitive to human triggers longer.

- Since they remain weak longer, they accumulate thicker slabs which, when they release, result in larger, more destructive avalanches.

- Layers of facets, depth hoar and surface hoar undergo brittle fracture over a wider range of conditions than non-persistent weak layers, making them more sensitive to human triggering.

The percentage of fatal avalanches for the various types of weak layers is summarised in the Fig. 2.22. In 14% of the accidents the weak layer was identified as "old" but the grain type was not reported.

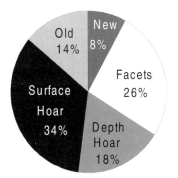

*Fig. 2.22 Percentage of fatal accidents by grain type of failure plane for 55 fatal accidents between 1972 and 1991.*

## Summary of Factors Common to Recreational Accidents

Many recreational accidents occur when the weather is pleasant: generally clear skies, little or no snowfall and light or calm winds.

Most of the avalanches are dry slab avalanches, with an average thickness of less than 100 cm, and most are triggered by victims or members of the victim's party. The weak layer often consists of surface hoar, facets or depth hoar.

The majority of accident avalanches start above or near tree-line on lee or cross-loaded slopes. The ground cover is often rocky. Most start on 30-40° slopes, often at a convex part of the slope.

Awareness of these factors and others described in this chapter may help recreationists select terrain appropriate to the snowpack and weather conditions. Since the interaction between snowpack and terrain can be subtle, route selection and stability assessment remain crafts learned over many years.

*Fig. 2.23 Many recreational avalanche accidents happen when the weather is fair. Torsten Geldsetzer photo.*

# Residential, Industrial and Transportation Accidents

As mentioned earlier, residential, industrial and transportation accidents have decreased during this century, but they still constitute a significant burden on our society. The few fatalities that have occurred in this category of accidents are of course the main concern. However, a notable aspect to many of the accidents is the financial loss associated with them. This can take the form of lost or damaged property, manpower costs of repairing damage and, less obviously, the loss of revenue due to delays caused by avalanches. Avalanches that affect highways account for the majority of residential, industrial and transportation accidents. However, highways often have the most active control programs to deal with the problem.

## Fatalities

Over the past 12 years there have only been two reported cases in which avalanches have hit residential areas and where people were killed. There were three fatalities in total. No fatalities have occurred on roads or in any industrial facility in Canada for the past 12 years.

## Monetary Costs

To come up with a dollar figure for the total property loss due to avalanches is very difficult. At best we can estimate. Even then we probably fall short due to the number of accidents that go unreported each year. Some vehicles or structures that are damaged are very expensive to replace or repair and constitute the majority of the cost figure. For example, repairing or replacing a damaged power line tower may run as high as $1 000 000. In addition there are the smaller items such as damaged automobiles, damaged snowmobiles and lost skis.

Based on reports between 1979 and 1985 Schaerer (1987, p. 6) estimates the average cost of property damaged by avalanches to approximate $350 000 per year in Canada. This does not include lost revenue. For example, up to $50 000/day could be attributed to lost revenue while a powerline is being repaired.

## Avalanches on Highways

Road closures present another cause for lost revenue. Delays for shipping companies, for example, not only cost the retailer time and money but ultimately this cost is carried forward to the consumer. Morrall and Abdelwahab (1992) estimate that a two-hour closure at Rogers Pass costs between $50 000 and $90 000. Consequently, the cost of avalanche delays on highways throughout western Canada exceeds the cost of damage to structures and equipment each winter.

Most avalanches that reach the highways are initiated by control programs and do not pose a threat to the public because the roads are closed at these times. Although these control measures are in place to minimise the threat, occasionally natural avalanches do cross open roads. On average about 10 automobiles become involved with avalanches each year. Most of the involvements are cases in which automobiles run into avalanche debris that has been deposited on the road. Fewer cases exist where a moving automobile has been hit by a moving avalanche. In 244 cases in which an avalanche did reach a road, the median length of road totally or partially covered by an avalanche deposit was 31 m. Seventy percent of these started as slab avalanches and most of them involved dry snow.

## Survival Factors

When we travel in avalanche country we accept the risk of possibly being caught and perhaps buried in an avalanche. What are our chances of surviving an avalanche? About 86%. This number depends on a number of factors. Luck is one of them, as is our ability to stay near the surface by getting rid of anything that could anchor us down and by struggling to stay on the surface. The terrain, the size of the avalanche and the depth of burial determine where and in what condition a victim might end up. That leaves the most important factor: the time

before a buried person is uncovered. This depends on the rescuers (the group members) and the rescue equipment and their training.

## Terrain and Cause of Death

Certain terrain features increase the consequences of being caught in an avalanche. Cliffs and trees in the path increase the odds of traumatic injuries. In 66 cases in which the cause of death is known, 32% were due to trauma. The other 68% died of asphyxiation due to burial. At least half of the trauma victims were the result of being carried over cliffs or through trees.

## Avalanche Size

The mass, speed and density of the moving snow combined with the distance it travels and what type of terrain it travels through will determine the destructive potential of the avalanche (for a detailed description of the size, see Appendix B). Fig. 2.24 shows that the chance of surviving an avalanche decreases as the size of the avalanche increases. The graph includes those involved even in a minor way with the avalanche.

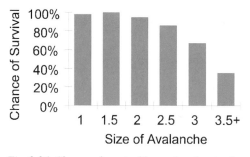

*Fig. 2.24 Chance of survival by avalanche size for 711 people caught or buried in avalanches between October 1984 and September 1996.*

## Depth and Duration of Burial

Increased depth and duration of burial reduce a victim's chances of survival (Figs. 2.25 and 2.26). However, the graphs exaggerate the consequences since a higher proportion of fatal accidents are reported than non-fatal accidents.

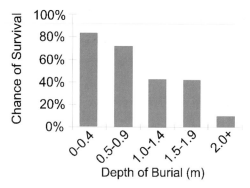

*Fig. 2.25 Chance of survival by depth of burial for 130 burials (that reported burial depth) between October 1984 and September 1996.*

The depth of burial depends on the size of the avalanche, the terrain in the run-out zone and the victim's ability to stay near the snow surface. The deeper a victim is buried the longer it will take to dig them out once they are located. Deeper burials also constrict breathing more due to the weight of the overlying snow.

The longer the burial, the smaller are the chances of survival. Little air permeates through the dense snow in an avalanche deposit and asphyxiation soon occurs. Making an air pocket in front of one's mouth will increase the amount of air available and may provide those extra few minutes needed for the group to uncover the victim. The duration of burial depends heavily on the ability of the group to locate and uncover the victim. This, in turn, depends strongly on the equipment and training they have.

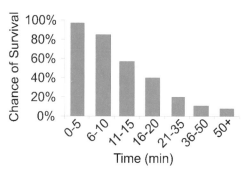

*Fig. 2.26 Chance of survival by duration of burial for 114 burials (that reported burial duration and either survived or died from asphyxia) between October 1984 and September 1996.*

# Search and Rescue

The best, if not only, chance a buried person has for survival is for rescue by the other members of the group. A buried victims is unlikely to survive if the others in their group has to seek the assistance of a rescue agency. This means that the group has to be prepared to carry out their own search and rescue. Fig. 2.27 shows the most common methods by which buried persons have been located. To date, avalanche dogs have not made a live recovery in Canada because it takes considerable time for the dog and master to be notified and then brought to the accident site.

Avalanche transceivers are the most effective method of locating a buried victim and recreationists must make a habit of wearing them when travelling in the backcountry. Tragically, 75% of all people that died while participating in non-commercial recreation were not wearing avalanche transceivers. Hopefully, through education and increased awareness, the number of people wearing transceivers will increase and thereby increase the number of buried people found alive.

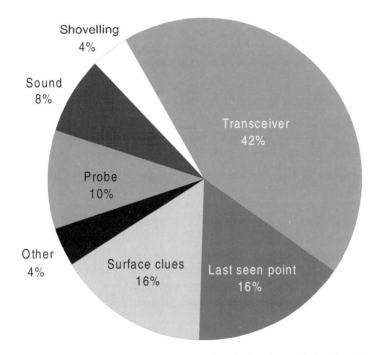

*Fig. 2.27 Percentage of completely buried persons found alive by method of location for 51 complete burials (that reported the location method) between October 1984 and September 1996.*

# Chapter 3

# First-Person Account of an Avalanche Accident and Self-Rescue

by

## Scott C. Berry

To be sitting here now, weeks after the "incident", weeks of putting off writing this down, now that the true emotions of time are memories, it all seems so anti-climatic.

I can remember that night, after the avalanche, being in the shelter, drowning in an ocean of diverse feelings, wondering what the next day would hold. The night before, I had been in a cheap but cozy hotel room in Lake Louise with my brother Jon and my friend Rene.

It was at this point that we anticipated a day of virgin powder and untracked trails. I envisioned ourselves in the Bow Hut the following night, but this was not to be, due to a cruel twist of fate. We joked with our usual repartee. That night I slept well.

The next day we awoke to some light falling snow and a sharp crispness that foretold of frozen valleys, crackling trees and glistening peaks. We cooked ourselves a quick breakfast in the basement of the hotel. The sky was just beginning to lighten at the time, beckoning to all winter adventurers.

After engineering our packs, skis and bodies into Rene's eastern-built compact, we hopped over to the warden's office for the information we needed about weather conditions and avalanche activity. We found ourselves behind a large counter in a typical government office, plastered with pamphlets on "how not to feed bears" as well as maps that showed the area from every point of view including 3-D, space shots, and the usual green topo views.

The woman on the other side of the counter looked up at us with a smile that gave away her true feelings about being up this early and having to talk to some pile-clad, bright-eyed winter-mongers. We were simply told that the skiing couldn't be better, but she wasn't really sure, having never been to the Bow Hut before and not really an off-trail hiker.

This could do nothing but wet our appetites even more for the snow and vast icefields. So once again we piled back into the transport buggy and headed off up the Icefields Parkway to the Num-Ti-Jah entrance. Upon arriving, we noticed that the wind was strong and unrelent-

ing off the lake. The drifts around the lake were large, but we were hungry for backcountry powder. It wasn't long before we had gathered our gear together, checked our avalanche transceivers, strapped on our shovels, axes and probe poles and headed off down the Num-Ti-Jah Lodge road to the Bow Lake shoreline. The pace was moderate but smooth, with each of us trading off leads across the lake. A few times the blowing snow obscured the guy in front who was usually only five to ten meters ahead.

In no time we found ourselves at the entrance of a windswept crystal palace where the lake narrowed to a chasm that was unpassable along its base. We stopped here for a quick rest and discussed methods of surviving in an avalanche, and how to locate buried skiers. It seemed so routine, I had done it so many times, relating what my training and all my readings had taught me. We were all well prepared and practised; we would and could confront the growing blizzard ahead of us. We felt indestructible, invincible and stubborn. Our determination saw no bounds; our goals were our obsessions and nothing could stop us.

As we began to plod through knee-deep powder, the pace slowed to a crawl. We finally located the ancient packed trail which had two feet of fresh snow on top. It was like walking a frozen tight-rope, where, if you strayed off the trail, you found yourself wallowing in deep drifts.

As soon as we emerged from the trees, we found ourselves at the base of the first avalanche bowl. We crossed this slope, one at a time until we fought our way out and on to the top of a knoll. We had our first close-up view at this time of the immense, hanging Bow Glacier and Bow Falls. The sight in front of us was spectacular: a symphony of winter was before us. There were hanging seracs, rolling moraine, huge frozen waterfalls and a whirlwind of snow all around. We felt that we only had to enter this to be as one with it, and subsequently we were. In no time we had crossed the moraine and confronted the doorway of the gully that later would be one of the biggest

nightmares of our lives. Unsuspecting as we were, we headed into the mouth of the chasm and began our plod to its end.

Our cautions had increased and we were on the lookout for signs of danger. There had been no distant rumblings and no jumbles of snow that indicated previous avalanche activity. On route we exited once too early and regained the gully. Our guidebook was vague and brief. We finally found what appeared to be the exit and we quickly entered onto a large open avalanche slope that appeared secure. The slope shone like the train of a wedding veil flowing down the aisle. It was at this point that we could see our objective. Ahead hung the huge drooping glacier that clung to the immense cliffs surrounding the Bow Hut.

Rene was in front, about 50 m ahead of Jon, who was about 70 m ahead of me. Feeling the excitement of almost being there, I sped up. My stride quickened as I approached Jon and suddenly I was swept down the slope, engulfed in tons of snow. Over and over I turned; everything was so quick. It was just as I started to slow down that I realised we all were caught. I was drifting slowly down the hill on my back, head downhill in the avalanche until eventually I stopped, and it began to compress around me like wet cement, forcing its way into every air pocket available. I managed to get one arm free and keep the snow off my face. When it all stopped, I lay there for a few seconds to let the realisation sink in. I let out a yell, shot my arm up into the air—there was no answer. I yelled again and again, but no responses. Horror struck me; the other two must be completely buried—so fast—without warning. My only hope lay in my ability to free myself from this snowy grave. I worked feverishly, digging first my other arm out, then my torso. At this point I realised that one of my skis was still attached and I would have to reach my binding to break free. This proved to be extremely frustrating, but I finally managed to open it with one of my poles that I was able to save.

Finally I was free. I heard a muffled cry to my right. As I approached, I noticed Jon in the same position as I had been in, but with both his arms pinned behind him. I brushed snow

off his face and looked at him. His eyes were wide, but he had a determination in him that showed through. When I was first approaching him, I managed to catch a glimpse of a ski and boot about 50 metres up the slope. I told Jon this and began his excavation immediately. I had him out in minutes. Once free, I grabbed my shovel and ran up the slope over the rubbled snow to where Rene must be. Jon was quickly behind me. We dug frantically and found his leg, torso, and shoulder, but couldn't find his head. I looked at Jon and said, "Be prepared." We found his face! It was as blue as ice; blue as death. I asked Jon to begin artificial respiration. Rene immediately began very shallow and raspy breathing. This put some hope into both of us. We quickly uncovered the rest of him and began to drag his body to a more secure location in the trees.

Rene later related that he could feel snow being pushed up his back, between his shirt and skin, and that he was frustrated because he didn't know how to stop it. The sensation, he explained, was terrifying, with no control of his own environment—like being paralysed. We got Rene off the avalanche slope and into a treed area next to the slide path. We immediately fired up our stoves and proceeded to remove Rene's wet clothing and put him inside our sleeping bags. As Jon began to warm some hot chocolate, I began the process of warming Rene, who at this point was dropping quickly into lower levels of hypothermia. He had begun violent shivering and then stopped, which is actually a bad sign. I immediately crawled in next to him to reverse this process as quickly as possible. He was incoherent and mumbling to himself. Eventually he began to shiver again and regain some consciousness. After approximately 45 minutes of this slow recovery, he opened his eyes and wondered what had happened and if everybody was okay. I explained to him the situation and reassured him that we were all fine and would get out of this situation successfully. At this point we began to feed him small sips of hot chocolate and keep him warm. This now enabled one of us to search the slide for our equipment while the other observed Rene. Jon went to dig first and dis-

covered two of the packs and two skis. After approximately half an hour, I traded with Jon and found the other pack and three more skis and three poles, but nothing else. Jon went back and checked again through the snow, but was unable to locate anything more. Every time we went back onto the slope it felt as though we were walking around inside the gaping mouth of a large wintery beast that could snap its jaws closed at any moment. Even though we knew that the slope was probably safer than it had been before the slide, we couldn't help but keep one eye on the slope above us at all times.

Three hours after the avalanche had swept us down, we were back on our feet again ready to fight our way home. Rene seemed fine now. He put on some dry clothes and became a participating member of our team once again. After some debate with little argument we decided to retrace our steps back to a heavily wooded area that we had passed through earlier, and attempt to build a shelter there and bed down for the night. Once again we had to cross this slope with our heads cocked to one side. We finally reached the other side after what seemed like an eternity. The going was rather easy considering we had only four skis and three poles between us. As soon as we entered the trees Jon and I found ourselves waste-deep in bottomless snow that had grown quite heavy from the warmer temperatures that were normally prevalent at this time of the day. Rene broke trail ahead of us on two skis while Jon and I attempted to walk on his tracks with one foot, and ski with the other. We travelled far enough so that we were well out of danger's way.

We looked for a deep tree-moat and used this as a base for our shelter. Because of the fast approaching nightfall and Rene's condition, which mostly consisted of a bad headache at this point, we chose not to build a *quinzhee* shelter. The tree-moat would allow us to build something rather quickly and get out of the blizzard which was still increasing in intensity. We all were all very concentrated on the task at hand and had very little time to reflect on the events that had just unfolded. We dug an emergency tarp out of one of the packs to use as a roof and widened the base of the moat for three

people. We tied the tarp to the tree and spread it like a circus tent. We built some walls of snow and draped the edge of the tarp over the walls. We then filled in the holes with snow and conifer branches from the surrounding trees. Eventually we had an effective shelter to protect us through the night and give us a sense of security.

We now had time to think about our ordeal, but the only conversation that we could muster consisted of statements like "We were lucky" and "It's not over yet". That was the truth; it was not over! We had a long way to go and needed all the resources we could utilise. We had a quick dinner as things began to get dark and then arranged ourselves within the shelter like sardines, lying on our sides. At least it was warm in there; maybe too warm. We had to make the opening wider to let some of the warmth out.

We lay there for hours without talking, without sleeping, just reflecting, and the more we reflected the more we realised how precious life really is. The emotions overtook us all in their own way, but nothing was held back, and that was good. It meant that we would probably be able to come to terms with what had happened and deal with it in our own way. Some sleep eventually came, but it was intermittent and interspersed with muffled cries of alarm as we each re-experienced the previous day's events.

Finally there was light, but it was subdued as it was still snowing heavily and looked as though it was not going to let up. We arose from our berth and began to ready ourselves for the excursion back to the car, which seemed a long way off—a very long way off. We discussed whether we should attempt to extricate ourselves out of this predicament or wait until we were overdue and be rescued by a chopper. We decided that a helicopter would not be able to fly in this weather and that it would mean spending another night out in this blizzard. We chose to leave.

The next decision was the route. Should we follow the summer trail along the top of the gully or risk travelling through the base again? After attempting the summer route for half an hour and sinking up to our chests in bottomless snow, we opted for the harder pack of the gully bottom. We found an exit that dropped down into the usual winter route. The going wasn't much better. Rene would go on ahead and break trail while Jon and I would attempt to follow in his tracks, which consisted of moving one ski ahead and then shifting all the weight to this one ski which would promptly sink to knee level, then throw the foot forward with no ski on it and shift the weight to that foot which would end up sinking to hip level, and then repeating this all over again. It was certainly one of the most exhausting things I have ever had to attempt over a long period of time. The other problem this created was that we were constantly breaking the tension in the slab. To reduce the risk, we crossed each open slope into the gully one at a time. Rene would cross the gully first and then stop and watch while either Jon or myself crossed next. On one of the particularly large gullies, Jon was crossing last and in the middle of the slope the whole thing fractured, but did not release. If it had released, Jon would definitely have been buried. This kept us on edge constantly. We did not look forward to our turn to cross the gully. It was like walking the gauntlet. After a couple of hours of this, we had one more sensitive part to cross. Rene crossed first and waited, then I crossed and waited, and then Jon crossed and once again, half way across the slope it fractured, but this time it released. I yelled "AVALANCHE!", and Jon somehow managed to almost run across the surface of the snow. The edge of the slab crossed the back of Jon's one ski, but failed to grab him. The snow piled up so high above our tracks that we estimated it to be at least 2 metres above the surface of the snow, which meant that anyone caught in it would have been buried a long way under.

That was it: The worst danger seemed over. We could see the mouth of the canyon that opened up to the windswept moraine that had so awed us the day before. Now it was like paradise; it was one of the most beautiful places I had ever seen.

Although the danger was mostly behind us, we still had a long way to go. We removed the skis we had on and walked across the moraine to the knoll we had stood on the previous day. Instead of traversing one more avalanche slope we took a route straight over the top of the wooded hill between the avalanche slope and the unpassable chasm. This turned out to be the worst snow slogging we had experienced yet. Because we were now walking we were in snow that reached our stomachs. This eventually led to us crawling on our hand and knees until we could slide down the other side of the hill to the start of the outwash plain before Bow Lake. We now realised that we would probably all make it out alive. We dropped our packs and gear and began hugging each other and shaking hands and saying thanks. Nothing else mattered then but being alive.

We walked to the shore of the lake and began our journey across to the other side which we couldn't see because of the high winds and the blowing snow. In fact when we were in the middle of the lake we had to support each other from being blown down by the wind which seemed to be gusting at 150 km/h. The snow was like needles and the wind was like thunder in our ears. It seemed as though this place was not ready to let us go just yet. It still had its icy fingers hanging onto our bodies, but we were strong. Our determination to get home was stronger than nature's strongest fury. We climbed a huge snow drift near the lodge and slid down the other side to asphalt. On one side of the parking lot was an older fellow in a large snowplow, clearing the parking lot. He looked at us for a second with inquiring eyes and then went back to his work. We didn't want to stop to tell him what had happened, we just wanted to get away from there as fast as possible.

Rene's car now resembled a limousine instead of the compact foreign car that it was. After we packed our gear and piled it and ourselves in, we started on down the highway to Lake Louise. Everything looked new and full of life. The sun came out and illuminated the peaks all around. It was a welcoming reward for surviving. Eventually we arrived back at the warden's office and went upstairs to sign in. The same woman was there and began to go through the routine of signing us back in, but looked at us inquiringly when we all just sat there grinning. Finally we began to tell her what happened. She interrupted us to get some wardens to listen. After telling the story and answering all their questions, one of the wardens said, "You've had a terrible experience, but don't let it prevent you from going out there again; there is a lot to discover and a lot the mountains can offer you if you let them."

After all the formalities we were on our way again back to Calgary, talking, laughing, reflecting. Near Calgary, Rene was pulled over for speeding. The police officer gave us all a strange look when we smilingly thanked him for the ticket.

In June I went back up to the spot myself. Almost all of the snow was gone and the day was sunny and hot. I walked into the location in about one and half hours, and was stunned. It really was a beautiful spot. The river was cascading in the chasm below; the birds were singing; the sun was warm. It wasn't the way I remembered it. The first thing that caught my eye was a ski sticking up in the snow beside the trail and a broken pole. Someone had spotted the ski and stuck it upright in the snow. But there was no sign of the rest of the equipment which still lay buried underneath the remaining snow. I constructed a weather-proof sign explaining what had happened and that there was still some equipment under the snow. I fastened it to a tree and left. About three weeks later a man contacted me and said he had found the remaining skis and poles and had brought them out. This seemed to complete the episode, yet it still lingers in my mind. We proved to ourselves that we could survive. We all grew after that, maybe in different ways, but I think we became more optimistic and gained a greater appreciation for life. Most important of all we are more active than ever in our outdoor pursuits, but the avalanche was nature's warning to us to never underestimate the potential of its power.

**Comment:** This remarkable account, combined with subsequent talks with the author, illustrate some important points:

- The heavy snowfall, drifting snow and warming temperature, combined with the avalanche prone terrain in the Bow Canyon could have been the basis for turning around.

- They were spaced out—about 70 m from the first person to the last—when the 110 m wide avalanche released. Had they spaced further apart while crossing the avalanche slope above the canyon, only one person might have been caught.

- All three skiers had the belts from their heavy packs buckled around their waists, and hands in their pole straps. This probably impaired at least one skier's struggle in the avalanche, causing his hands to be pinned behind him so he could not make a space in front of his face or dig himself out.

- They had non-releasable telemark bindings and their skis stayed on, making movement in the avalanche more difficult.

On the other hand, they:

- checked in with the warden service and obtained current information before starting,

- reviewed avalanche rescue prior to entering the canyon,

- spaced themselves apart while crossing avalanche slopes,

- effectively treated Rene for hypothermia,

- bivouacked in difficult conditions, and

- kept their spirits up and successfully rescued themselves.

# Chapter 4

# Skiing and Snowboarding Accidents

## Wawa Bowl, Banff National Park

27 December 1984

- **one backcountry skier killed**
- **recent snowfall and wind loading**
- **no transceivers**

| Weather Conditions at Sunshine Ski Village Elevation 2145 m, 1.5 km southeast of accident site | | | | | | |
|---|---|---|---|---|---|---|
| Date 1984 | Time | Max. Temp. (°C) | Min. Temp. (°C) | Snowfall (cm) | Snowpack Height (cm) | Wind (km/h) |
| 12-25 | 0800 | -11 | -14 | 10 | 132 | 29 - S |
| 12-25 | 1430 | -9 | -12 | 4 | 136 | 21 - S |
| 12-26 | 0800 | -9 | -11 | 22 | 146 | 32 - SW |
| 12-26 | 1600 | -11 | -11 | 1 | 144 | 29 - SW |

On December 27th two men left the Sunshine ski area boundary to ski Wawa Bowl about 1 km to the northwest. This east-facing bowl is at treeline in the Rocky Mountains of Banff National Park.

In the preceding 2 days, the air temperature had remained cool (-9° to -16°C) but 39 cm of snow had fallen, including 22 cm on the night of December 25th. South and southwest winds had loaded lee slopes including much of Wawa

Bowl. Snowfall and wind-blown snow had loaded a weak layer of faceted crystals approximately 1 m above the ground.

After the first run on the skier's left side of the bowl, the two men ascended for a second run closer to the centre of the bowl. While belayed by his partner, Skier 1 approached a convex roll where the slope steepened. He dug a pit to assess snow stability and jumped on the top of the slope to test it. He then skied down the slope to a safe place and motioned for his partner to follow. Skier 2 fell twice and was skiing near the middle of the slope when he triggered a 120 cm-thick slab, 130 m wide. After moving about 20 m, the size 2.5 slab avalanche stepped down to the ground, gathering more snow. Skier 2 was observed in the moving avalanche by his partner until he was completely buried near the toe of the deposit (Fig. 4.1).

Skier 1 went to the burial site and located his partner after probing for 15 minutes. After removing approximately 1 m of overlying snow, he found his partner unresponsive. He began CPR and continued until park wardens happened onto the scene. They evacuated the victim by helicopter to hospital in Banff where he was pronounced dead.

**Source:** Banff Park Warden Service

**Comment:** Although the recent snowfall and wind loading were conducive to avalanches, the skiers approached the slope carefully, digging a pit and testing the slope. They skied it one at a time and Skier 1 stopped in a safe place. Without these safety measures, both skiers may have been caught.

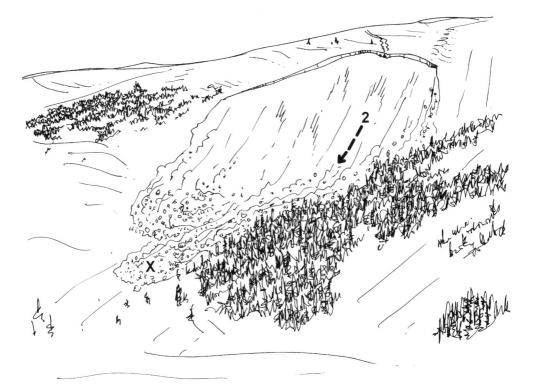

*Fig. 4.1  Wawa Bowl, 84-12-27. The first skier was at the bottom of the slope and not caught in the avalanche. 2 - location of second skier when avalanche started. X - location of second skier's body after the avalanche.*

Skier 1 observed the last seen point and was able to locate the victim after 15 minutes of probing. However, the victim had already died of suffocation.

Due to snowpack variability, slope tests are sometimes misleading as illustrated by the skiing accidents of 16 March 1993 and 29 March 1993 in this chapter. Also, the "pit" may have been on top or too close to the top of the slope to show the weaknesses present in the bowl. Profiles done at the crown and at the nearby Wawa Bowl Study Plot after the accident showed an easy shovel shear approximately 1 m above the ground (Fig. 4.2).

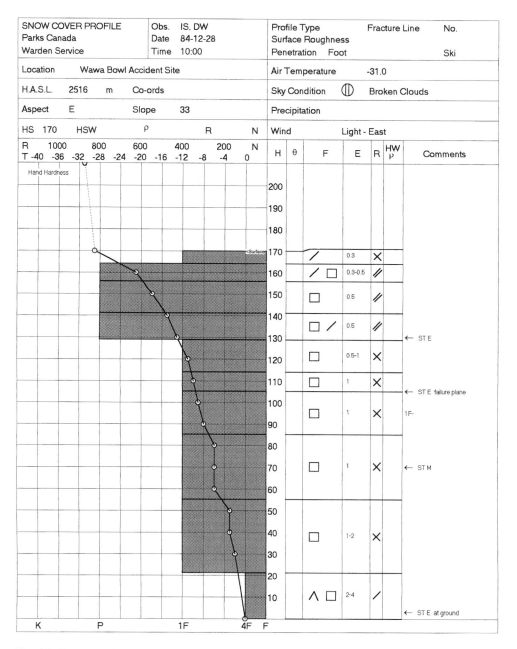

*Fig. 4.2 Wawa Bowl, 84-12-27. Profile observed just above crown one day after the accident showing easy shear in failure plane.*

# Mount Neptune, near Rossland, BC

29 December 1984

- **two helicopter skiers killed**
- **shallow snowpack areas prone to faceting**
- **exposed location for regrouping**

It was about ten o'clock in the morning when the group of six skiers landed on the 2165 m summit of Mount Neptune near Rossland, British Columbia. After getting out of the helicopter they looked down onto the eastern slope of Mount Neptune. Some of them had skied the slope a few hundred meters further south the day before. The guide, an apprentice guide in training, advised his group to ski the slope one at a time and regroup at the bottom. He went first, doing a series of ski cuts at the top of the slope to test the snow stability and then, satisfied, skied down to what he considered a safe spot.

About 10 cm of new snow had fallen overnight and the wind was light from the southwest. Looking back to December 15th, there had been a little-known inversion at the mountain tops and a period of freezing rain had formed a thin crust. Following this, the temperatures had fluctuated between -2 and -23°C and it had snowed, off and on, accumulating 74 cm. The colder temperatures had caused some faceting in the snowpack, especially just below the crust which acted as a vapour barrier. The trees near the summit had some rime build-up on their south-facing side, evidence of a south wind that had cross-loaded the slope.

Once the guide reached the bottom, Skier 2 started down. When he was about three quarters of the way down he triggered a size 2.5 avalanche. It fractured above and to his right, breaking up to within 15 m of the ridge line. There were several large granite boulders buried just below the ridge. On these the snow was relatively shallow and they acted as weak points that connected the fracture line. The avalanche broke out over a width of 100 m and ran down the slope for about 200 m. It slid on a layer of faceted crystals at depths varying from 40 to 80 cm, just below the mid-December rain crust.

It ran very quietly. Skier 2 was immediately swept away. The guide saw the avalanche start and, realising that he was in its path, tried to ski out of its way, but it was moving much too fast and he was engulfed as well. Both skiers were buried with their heads pointing downhill, angled deeper into the slope, while their boots ended up just a little below the snow surface (Fig. 4.3).

The four skiers at the top of the slope, as well as another group of four skiers also on the ridge, switched their transceivers to receive and skied down the avalanche path to the deposit. Once there, they located the two buried skiers and dug them out. Both were not breathing and had no pulse so CPR was initiated. One of the rescuers, another guide, radioed the helicopter which came and transported the victims and rescuers to a nearby hospital while CPR was continued. Both skiers were pronounced dead on arrival at the hospital. The guide had died from asphyxiation and Skier 2 had died from trauma, which he likely received from being carried through some small trees while in the moving avalanche. The total time between the avalanche occurrence and arrival at the hospital was only about half an hour.

**Source:** Jack Bennetto, BC Ministry of Transportation and Highways

**Comment:** Subtle variations in terrain and snowpack structure can make the difference between a stable and unstable slope. Boulders on a slope can act as anchors, but once they are covered, the snow on top of the boulders is much shallower than the surrounding snow and is therefore much more susceptible to the weakening, faceting process with cold temperatures. Wind action can have a similar effect. A slope that is more windward can be scoured, thereby

reducing the depth of that particular region of the snowpack. This shallower snowpack is, again, more susceptible to the growth of facets.

Whenever possible, sites for stability evaluations should be chosen that are representative of the slope to be skied. However, isolated weaknesses cannot always be determined and they can present a risk that cannot be eliminated.

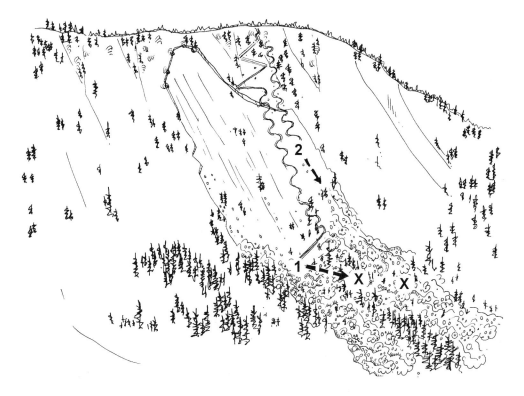

*Fig. 4.3 Mount Neptune, 84-12-29. 1 - initial position of guide. 2 - second skier. X - deceased. Eight other skiers were on top of ridge.*

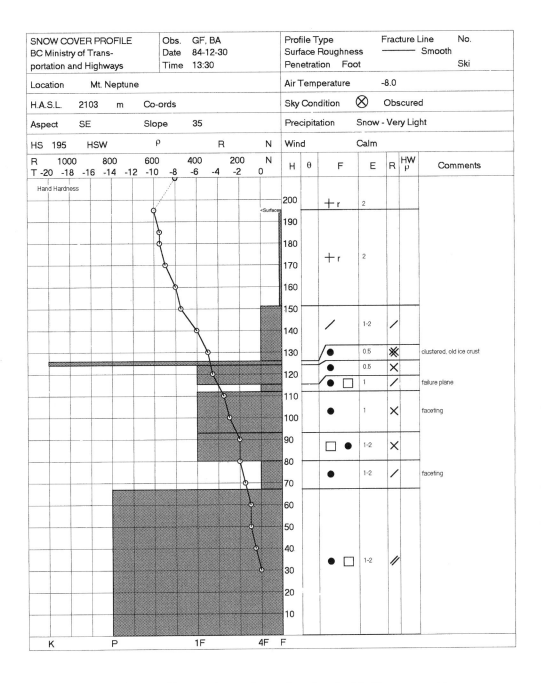

*Fig. 4.4  Fracture line profile was observed  one day after the Mt. Neptune accident.*

# Mt. Duffy, Monashee Mountains

18 February 1985

## • two helicopter skiers killed crossing gully

On February 18th towards the end of a day of helicopter skiing, a group of 12 skiers and a guide were skiing a south-facing slope on Mt. Duffy in the Monashee Mountains. Under overcast skies, they were enjoying approximately 20 cm of dry, low density snow that had fallen in the previous few days on top of a base that varied from settled snow to sun crust to a wind-hardened crust. A snow profile on Mt. Duffy found the storm snow to be bonded to a sun crust.

Avoiding a 35° slope that fed into a gully at about 2200 m, the group skied 200 m down a less steep slope to the east. Heading back toward the helicopter pickup, the guide traversed a bench in the gully where it was approximately 50 m wide. Although the guide had instructed the skiers to cross the gully one at a time, the sixth skier started across while the fifth was in the gully. A soft slab released 150 m above the traverse tracks and hit the fifth skier. The sixth skied into the moving avalanche.

The sixth skier was carried approximately 15 m and buried. The guide located him by transceiver within 5 minutes. Although most of his body was 1 m below the surface, searchers had to dig a 2 m-deep hole—that took an additional 10 minutes—since one of the victim's arms was held down by a ski pole strap. Other guides arrived and began CPR. The fifth skier was carried 120 m and buried under 1 m of snow. He was also located by transceiver and uncovered—without vital signs—approximately 20 minutes after the avalanche. Both victims received CPR while they were flown to the Blue River Outpost Hospital where they were pronounced dead. Subsequent autopsies found that both had asphyxiated.

The avalanche started where the wind had formed a 30 cm-thick slab, about 35 m wide, that slid on a wind-hardened bed surface. Below the start zone, the slab picked up the low density snow in the gully, resulting in a size 3 avalanche.

**Comment:** It is not known if the avalanche was triggered or started naturally. Nevertheless, if the sixth skier had waited until the fifth was across, at most one person would have been caught.

Ski pole straps and ski straps should generally not be used in avalanche terrain, since they impair an avalanche victim's ability to struggle towards the surface.

# Montagne Blanche, Quebec

3 March 1985

- **one backcountry skier killed**
- **poorly equipped**

On the afternoon of the 3rd a party of 12 skiers was returning from a tour around Montagne Blanche in the Charlevoix Mountains of Quebec. As they neared their camp they came upon an inviting slope just below treeline. One of the skiers started down, followed by a second skier who fell part way down. A third skier then entered the slope.

It had been very windy most of the day with estimated mountain-top winds of 70 km/h. This had kept the group from climbing up the mountain. The day before it had been raining, but by now the temperature had plummeted to -20°C.

Soon after the third skier started his descent, he triggered an avalanche near the top of the slope. The slab released on ice-covered rocks at the base of the snowpack to a depth of 1.5 m. It swept down the slope burying the fallen skier before he had time to get up. It then also caught the first skier but he managed to stay on the surface and ended up at the bottom unharmed. The fallen skier was not moved by the avalanche, but when the snow stopped he was lying face down, under 2 m of snow.

The trip leader quickly organised the rest of the group into a search party and they probed with their skis, moving downhill from where the fallen skier was last seen. After 10 minutes of searching they found one of his skis and continued searching. As the sun set, the temperature dropped even further, to -25°C, and the wind continued. The threat of frost-bite to the rescuers became a major concern. After 4 hours of probing and shovelling the search was called off. All of the party members had been kept at the site to help with the search, but now, with little hope of finding the buried skier alive, two people were sent to Anse St. Jean for help.

The following morning the Quebec Provincial Police arrived by helicopter. Their search dog located the buried skier's body 8 m uphill of where his ski had been found.

**Source:** Jean Rendeau, Federation Quebecoise de la Montagne

**Comment:** To have a chance of finding a buried person alive, the factor of time is the main consideration. The trip leader did well to keep everyone on site to aid in the search. The nearest help was 2 hours away, and by the time professional help would have arrived, it would have been too late. However, this case again illustrates the importance of wearing transceivers. The searchers might have found the fallen skier in time had they all been using them.

# White Queen Mountain, Nelson, BC

## 25 January 1986

- **one backcountry skier killed**
- **high avalanche hazard**

Two experienced backcountry skiers and a dog left the base of the Whitewater Ski Area near Nelson at 10:30 on January 25th. They toured toward White Queen Mountain, 1 km north of the ski area (Fig. 4.5). On their first run, they released a small slab while ski testing about half way down a south-facing slope. After a short run on the north side of White Queen Mountain, they returned to the south side. Concerned about the stability, they chose a more southwesterly slope over the south-facing run they had first skied. They hoped it had been warmed less by the sun during the day.

Between January 15-18th, 40-50 cm of snow fell in the Whitewater Ski Area and winds from the southwest gusted to 50 km/h. As the freezing level rose on the night of the 18th a mix of rain, graupel and snow fell at higher elevations. Numerous size 2 and 3 avalanches started naturally between 1900 m and 2000 m on the 19th. From January 19th to 25th, 23 cm of snow fell with light winds. From 07:30 to 14:30 on the 25th, the Whitewater Snow Safety team used hand charges and an avalauncher to release numerous size 2 and 2.5 avalanches. The slabs, 50-70 cm thick, ran on old facets and surface hoar. Temperatures in the ski area reached 0°C.

At 15:40 the two skiers descended through sparse trees and stopped above an open slope. The first skier skied over a convex roll, followed by his dog. Out of his partner's sight, he triggered a slab avalanche.

After calling out and not hearing a reply, the second skier approached the convex slope and found several cracks above a crown fracture. To get down to the first skier while avoiding the cracked area above the crown, he traversed into trees, descended part way down the slope and then traversed back onto the bed surface. Switching his transceiver to receive, he moved down the bed surface. He picked a signal up in trees below the open slope and while homing in on the signal, saw his partner's boot sticking out of the deposit. He quickly dug out his partner who was wrapped around a tree. From the traumatic injuries, he knew his partner was dead. He marked the location with flagging tape and skied out to the road below the ski area.

Whitewater Snow Safety staff had heard the avalanche from the ski area. They soon spotted the fracture line and then saw the surviving skier traversing towards the road. A staff member went down the road to meet the surviving skier, while others notified the RCMP and requested a search dog and helicopter.

With the surviving skier and rescue team on board, the helicopter flew to the deposit but was unable to land. They landed instead on top of the run and followed the ski tracks around the crown. At the deposit, they confirmed that the victim was dead. His body was picked up the next day. The dog was not found.

The 75 cm-thick slab released 25 m wide. According to a profile observed the next day, it had failed on old facets and surface hoar, 4 mm in size, that showed evidence of having melted and refrozen (Fig. 4.6). The bed surface was a crust. The size 3 avalanche ran down-slope for 580 m and deposited 2 m of snow in the trees.

**Source:** Tom Van Alstine, Nelson, BC

**Comment:** The tourers were experienced and well equipped. Also, they skied the slope one at a time. However, they started from the ski area where the posted avalanche hazard was *high*. It is not known if the tourers read the board where conditions are summarised and the hazard is posted. However, they did not speak to patrollers regarding conditions. The explosions from avalanche control could be heard during the day.

The two skiers chose to ski an open slope with a convex start zone rather than nearby tree skiing. The surviving skier stated "We gambled … and lost."

The fatal avalanche exposed boulders in the lower concave part of the start zone. The avalanche may have been triggered from well-developed facets and depth hoar that surrounded the boulders.

*Fig. 4.5  White Queen Mountain, 86-01-25. X - deceased.*

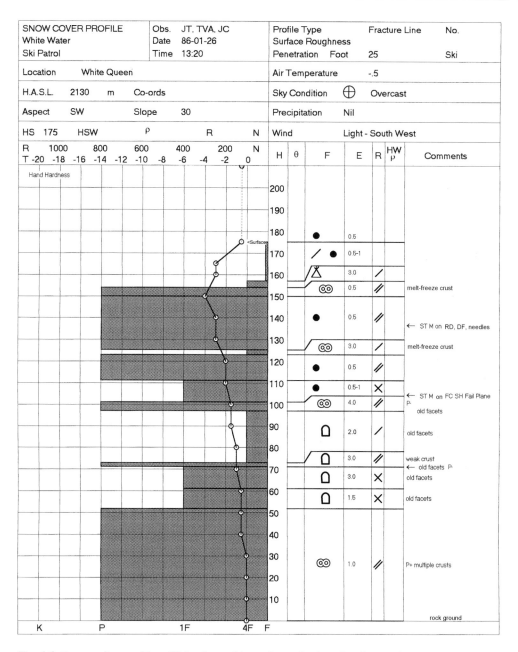

*Fig. 4.6 Fracture line profile at White Queen Mountain on the day after the accident.*

# Selkirk Mountains, Nakusp, BC

4 February 1986

- **two helicopter skiers killed**
- **persistent weak layer of facets and surface hoar**

On February 4th, two groups of helicopter skiers were skiing in the Selkirk Mountains east of Nakusp. At 14:40 they returned to a west-facing slope that they had skied twice in the morning. The first group of eleven skiers and a guide started down, skiing through open burnt trees just north of their tracks from the morning. Following instructions, the group was skiing to the left of the guide's tracks. Part way down the slope, a large slab avalanche released 100 m above the guide, sweeping him and the two closest skiers down the slope. At about the same time, a second avalanche released to the

south of the ski tracks from the morning. Nine skiers, between the larger avalanche and the previous tracks, were not caught (Fig. 4.7).

The remaining nine skiers were hesitant to descend to the deposit since avalanches had released on both sides. Some switched their transceivers to receive.

Unaware of the accident, a second group of helicopter skiers landed to ski the same slope. The guide from the second group soon saw the deposit and heard shouts from the nine skiers from the first group. Descending the slope, the guide from the second group spotted one partly

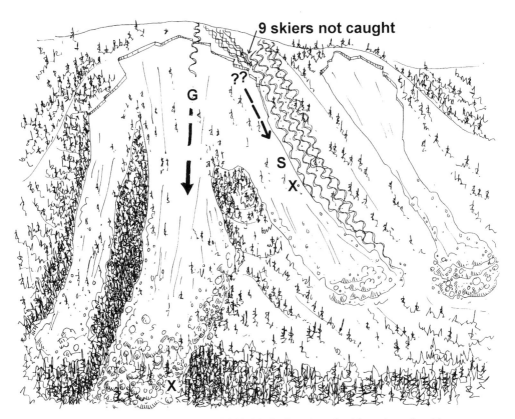

*Fig. 4.7 Selkirk Mountains east of Nakusp, 86-02-04. G - location of guide at time of accident. S - survivor. X - deceased.*

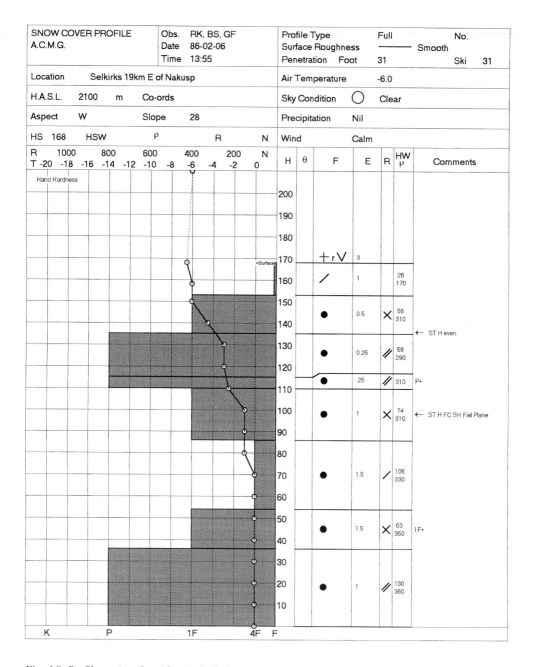

*Fig. 4.8  Profile at site of accident in Selkirk Mountains east of Nakusp, two days after the accident.*

buried skier—alive but injured—just inside the flank of the avalanche. With transceivers, searchers from both groups quickly located a signal 15 m down the slope from the injured skier. About 10 minutes after the avalanche, a skier was recovered from under about 70 cm of snow, but he was not alive.

While the partly buried and fully buried skiers were being located, a photographer from the second group searched the deposit to the north with his transceiver. He located a signal and began to dig for the buried guide from the first group. Soon, the guide from the second group arrived to join the digging. They uncovered the buried guide under 75 cm of snow, 20 minutes after the avalanche. Resuscitation efforts started at the scene and continued in the helicopter on the way to the Nakusp hospital where he was pronounced dead.

The size 3.5 avalanche started as a hard slab, 30-120 cm thick and 95 m wide. According to a profile done just above the crown two days later, the slab failed on a weak layer of facets and surface hoar (Fig. 4.8). The shovel shear test at the profile site was rated *hard*.

**Source:** ACMG Task Force and Ed LaChapelle

**Comment:** Persistent weak layers such as facets and surface hoar sometimes remain weak enough to release avalanches for a month or more. Once a fracture starts at a localised weakness, it can propagate along weak layers through areas where skiers could not trigger a fracture and where snowpack tests suggest stability. In this case, shovel tests of the weak layer ranged from *hard* at the profile site to *easy* at one point on the fracture line. It is because of this variability that profiles or snowpack tests at a few points on a slope can be misleading and should only be used in conjunction with other observations of avalanches, snowpack and weather.

In spite of the efficient rescue, both buried victims died. On slopes capable of large avalanches such as this one, transceivers, probes and shovels in well-trained hands improve the odds of—but do not assure—live recoveries.

# Coquihalla Lakes, Cascade Mountains, BC

17 February 1986

- **one backcountry skier killed while ascending on snowshoes**
- **obvious avalanche danger**
- **no transceivers, shovels or probes**
- **surface hoar**

| | | | | Weather Conditions at Coquihalla Summit | | | |
|---|---|---|---|---|---|---|---|
| | | | | Elevation 1230 m, 7 km southwest of accident site | | | |
| Date 1986 | Time | Max. Temp. (°C) | Min. Temp. (°C) | Snowfall (cm) | Storm Snow (cm) | Total Snowpack (cm) | Wind |
| 02-15 | 0650 | -5.5 | -11.5 | 7 | 7 | 163 | M - SE |
| 02-15 | 1630 | -11.0 | -12.0 | 12 | 18 | 178 | M - E |
| 02-16 | 0630 | -5.5 | -14.0 | 14 | 33 | 193 | M - E |
| 02-16 | 1600 | -7.0 | -12.5 | 11 | 41 | 202 | Calm |
| 02-17 | 0630 | -10.0 | -20.0 | 24 | 59 | 218 | Calm |
| 02-17 | 1245 | -16.0 | -20.5 | 4 | 60 | 218 | L - SE |

Two workers, employed on the construction of the Coquihalla Highway, wanted to ski the slopes above the highway on one of their days off work. They left the highway at 12:40 about 2 km southwest of Coquihalla Lakes. With skis strapped to their packs, they snowshoed up the southeast-facing slope beside the highway.

The Coquihalla Highway climbs over the Cascade Mountain Range, connecting Hope and Merritt, BC. In February 1986, the four-lane highway was still under construction. Clear weather prior to the 15th had caused the snow surface to become weak and faceted. In places, surface hoar crystals had grown on the snow surface. Starting on the 15th, heavy snowfall buried this weak layer of facets and/or surface hoar. By the morning of the 17th, 68 cm of snow had fallen on the weak layer.

The two workers snowshoed over one avalanche deposit and heard numerous "whumpfs" as fractures spread through the weak layer. About 200 m above the highway, they discussed returning because of the avalanche danger but decided to snowshoe up one more small slope before skiing down. As they traversed a bench, they triggered an avalanche on the slope above the bench. When the avalanche hit them, they were 8 m apart. The person behind tumbled once while being carried 12 m. He stopped face up under 30 cm of snow. Fortunately, he was able to push his arms to the surface and dig himself out (Fig. 4.9). All he could see on the deposit was a walking stick his partner had been using.

He had lost his poles and had to dig his skis and pack out of the snow. Using his skis as probes, he searched the deposit. While prob-

*Fig. 4.9 Coquihalla Lakes, 86-02-17. While ascending on snowshoes, the skiers triggered the avalanche from the bottom of the slope. S - survivor. X - deceased.*

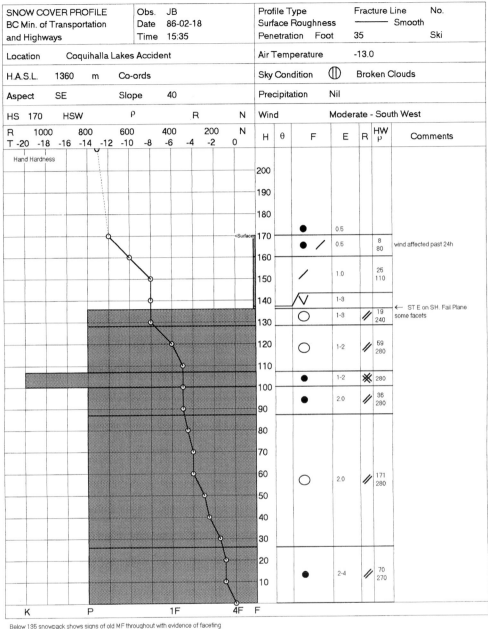

*Fig. 4.10  Fracture line profile at site of Coquihalla Lakes accident observed on the day after the avalanche.*

ing he hit something he thought might be his friend several times. However, when he dug down with his hands, he found only alder branches. Deciding to go for help, he skied to the highway and drove to the toll booth where he reported the accident at about 13:50. The

RCMP and Ministry of Transportation and Highways staff were notified. The RCMP dispatched a search dog and dogmaster from Chilliwack. As two Highways staff approached the site on touring skis, two others arrived by helicopter at 14:50. The victim was found af-

ter 5 minutes of probing and dug out 5 minutes later. Rescuers started CPR and continued it in the helicopter. A subsequent autopsy found that the victim had asphyxiated.

The 40-60 cm slab failed on a layer of surface hoar and faceted crystals. The 105 m wide slab started on a 40° slope and produced a size 2 avalanche that ran only 60 m. The 60 m by 30 m deposit had an average depth of 60 cm.

**Source:** BC Ministry of Transportation and Highways

**Comment:** A small amount of avalanche awareness training might have prevented this accident. The "whumpf" sounds and fresh natural avalanches clearly indicated the avalanche danger. However, the two men chose to go up "just one more slope" to get a better ski run down. Had the two skiers been further apart, only one would have been buried. The avalanche pushed the first victim 5 m and buried him face down under only 40 cm of snow. It is likely that a transceiver search could have saved his life.

---

# Assiniboine Provincial Park, BC

23 January 1987

### • one backcountry skier caught and injured

In January 1987, an avalanche course was held in Assiniboine Provincial Park, just west of the divide of the Rocky Mountains 34 km south of Banff, Alberta. During the week the students observed numerous snow profiles that showed a generally stable snowpack that varied from 70 to 150 cm in thickness. At 16:00 on January 23rd, four students and an instructor approached the top of a slope known as Jones' Leap.

They judged the snowpack to be relatively stable since the resistance of the snow above the slope increased with depth, no wind action was apparent on the slope, the adjacent slope had not been "slabby" when it was skied two days earlier, and they had not observed recent natural activity in the area. They decided to ski the slope because of these observations and because they would be taking safety measures on a relatively small slope. As the first skier unbuckled his waist belt and removed his pole straps, others positioned themselves so that they could see the slope below.

On the first turn, the skier's skis bogged down in deep soft snow. Then his skis rode up on top of a buried wind slab on his second turn. "I felt the snow consistency change radically. All of a sudden the snow started moving around

me." A wind slab released from 20 m above him. "I struggled to keep on top with all I had. I remember smacking all sorts of trees on the ride down….When it stopped, I popped my head up and started yelling, because of fright and pain."

The instructor skied down the bed surface after the slab, pausing part way down to ask the group to ski down. He found the victim with his hands and head out of the snow. The group removed snow from around the partly buried victim and assessed his injuries. Because of pain in his hip, they sent two skiers to the nearby lodge for help at 16:10 and assembled an improvised toboggan. After treating the injured skier for shock and his injuries, they pulled him in the improvised toboggan to the bottom of the slope. Teaming up with staff from the lodge who had brought a larger toboggan, they moved the victim to a clearing where they met a helicopter at 17:00. The victim was flown to hospital where tests revealed a pelvic fracture.

On a 37° slope, the skier had triggered a 30-40 cm-thick slab at an elevation of 2330 m. It released 6 m wide above him and broke out 12 m wide below the trigger point. Profiles two days later showed a *moderate* shovel shear in a weak layer of faceted crystals that were round-

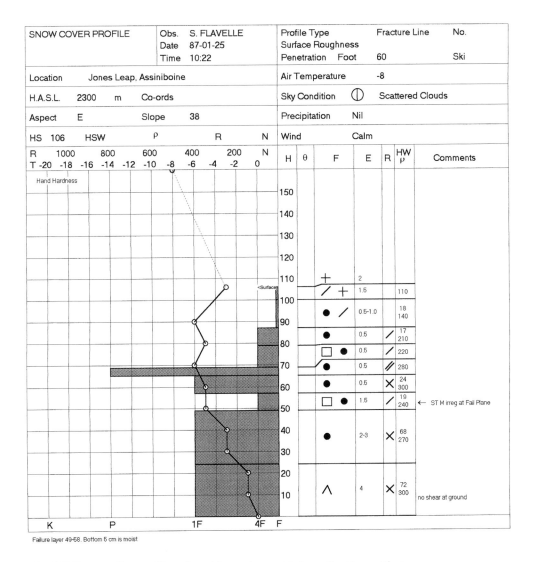

Fig. 4.11 Fracture line profile at Jones' Leap observed 2 days after the accident.

ing (Fig. 4.11). The size 2 avalanche ran 140 m and resulted in a 13 m-wide deposit that reached a maximum depth of 1.5 m.

**Source:** Clair Israelson

**Comment:** This case illustrates that even when the snowpack is generally stable, isolated pockets of unstable snow may exist.

Safety measures reduce either the probability of being caught, the consequences of being caught, or both. The slope was small enough to ski one at a time. By doing so, the group ensured that at most one person could get caught. The skier had removed his waist belt and pole straps. This facilitated the skier's struggle in the moving avalanche and probably helped him reach the surface of the deposit. In snow-covered avalanche terrain, safety measures reduce but do not eliminate the risks.

As a result of the efficient rescue including the improvised toboggan and help from the lodge, the victim met the helicopter in time to be flown to a hospital before dark.

# Gardner Creek, Selkirk Mountains

1 February 1987

- **one helicopter skier partially burial**
- **hand to surface**
- **new snow slab stepped down to old surface hoar layer**

On the morning of the February 1st, two guides for a heli-skiing company went out to assess the snow stability. They skied along a sparsely treed ridge, ski-cutting the slope to release about 30 cm of newly deposited snow from a hazardous area. The cut slabs were forming size 1 to 2 avalanches as they ran down the slope. The guides were skiing one at a time, from one island of safety to the next.

One of the guides had just triggered a slab 2 m below him when the moving slab triggered a deeper release some 2 to 3 seconds later. This one fractured over a width of 30 m and down to an old surface hoar layer 66 cm deep, forming a size 2.5 avalanche. Whereas the shallower new snow slabs had been releasing below the ridge crest, this slab pulled back to the ridge, right to the guide's tracks. The guide was caught and carried 200 m down the slope through burnt timber, just missing several trees. As the avalanche came to a stop he thrust one hand up to and through the surface of the snow — his head was 30 cm below the surface. The snow set up immediately, but with his free hand he was still able to clear an area down to his face. He could clearly hear his partner on the radio calling to the base, reporting the incident.

The second guide watched the avalanche from his safe vantage point and could see the first guide as he was being swept along, until he lost sight of him in the last 30 to 40 m. However, by looking from where he had last seen him and then further down the slope he spotted a moving hand sticking out of the snow in just a few seconds. He quickly skied down to his partner and it took three to four minutes of hard digging until he could finally pull him free. The buried guide was uninjured and felt most fortunate to be so.

A fracture line profile was done and showed the following results. The slope aspect was northwest with an incline of 33° and started at an elevation of 1920 m. The initial slab fractured down 29 cm, running on new and partially decomposed snow that had been lightly blown in. The surface hoar crystals the avalanche stepped down to, at 66 cm, were in the 2 to 5 mm range. Shovel tests gave *easy* results on both these layers. Most slopes 35° and steeper had released on the surface hoar the previous week or during the recent storm. However, many slopes below 35° had a lingering instability.

**Source:** Phil Hein, Columbia Mountain Recreation

**Comment:** This case highlights the importance of a number of concepts. Ski-cutting is a very serious undertaking on all but very small slopes. If caught in an avalanche, try to push one hand up towards the surface just before the snow stops moving—a visual reference is the fastest way for your partner(s) to find you. Keep the other members of your group in sight whenever you are in avalanche terrain and if someone is caught, try to follow their progress and determine the last seen point—knowing where to start searching will speed up the rescue tremendously. When a slope is suspect, minimise the number of people exposed to danger by skiing from one island of safety to the next. Be aware of not only the most obvious sliding layer, but also the deeper persistent weak layers.

# Thunder River, Cariboo Mountains

23 March 1987

- **seven helicopter skiers killed**
- **weak layer of surface hoar**
- **terrain trap**

On March 23rd, a group of nine skiers and a guide were helicopter skiing in the slopes above Thunder River in the Cariboo Mountains of BC. Shortly before 12:30, a helicopter dropped them off on a north-facing run at 2250 m, well above treeline. The guide planned to observe a snow profile on the slope to obtain further information about the snowpack stability.

In the preceding four days, the weather had been fair, with little fresh snow. At 06:00 at the Mt. St. Anne weather station (1900 m, Cariboos), the wind had been between 10 and 22 km/h and temperatures between -6.5 and -3°C. A surface hoar layer that formed around March 7th to 9th was buried, but had not produced any recent slab avalanches. The guides were monitoring the buried surface hoar with profiles and field tests, finding *hard* shears and uneven breaks.

Leaving the landing, three skiers lagged behind the guide and first six skiers. These six skiers were near the guide who was preparing to dig a pit when the slope released above them. The guide called "get out of the way" on his radio to warn the next group of helicopter skiers that were approaching the run. One of the three lagging skiers was pushed a short distance and buried waist deep. The guide and first six skiers were carried down the ski slope—about 250 m vertically—where they were buried in a large depression that extends across the slope (Fig. 4.12).

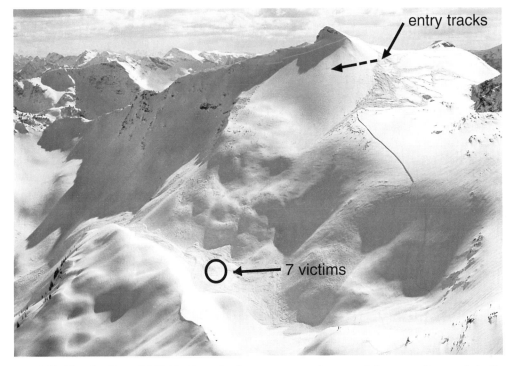

entry tracks

7 victims

*Fig. 4.12 Thunder River, 87-03-23. Extensive fracture propagation extended onto gentler terrain to the right of the main avalanche. Chris Stethem photo.*

The guide from the second group quickly organised the rescue using the three remaining skiers from the first group and the skiers from the second group. They found the signals from the victim's transceivers in the depression and began to dig. Other guides and their groups flew to the scene by helicopter to join the rescue. Shovelling took considerable time since the victims were buried 2-4 m deep in a dense deposit. The first victim was recovered 30 minutes after the avalanche and the last after three hours. All seven had asphyxiated and were pronounced dead at the scene.

The 70 cm-thick slab was 340 m wide. It slid on two-week old surface hoar crystals, 2-8 mm in length. The fracture also extended onto the west-facing slope where it released smaller avalanches.

**Comment:** This and other accidents have shown that layers of surface hoar can release slab avalanches many weeks after being buried. Also, hard slabs such as this one can propagate fractures over long distances and release large avalanches.

In spite of the efficient rescue, the terrain trap caused the victims to be deeply buried. Few people survive such deep burials.

---

# Bow Summit, Banff National Park

29 May 1987

- **one backcountry skier killed**
- **soft wet snow**

On May 29th, two skiers decided to ski the slopes above the old fire lookout at Bow Summit, 30 km northwest of Lake Louise. They looked at the slopes from the highway and picked the descent routes they wanted to ski. However, they hiked too far up the north ridge and prepared to ski a convex shaped slope in a 40° gully. At 16:15, while one stood on a rock outcrop taking pictures, the other started to ski. The soft isothermal snow failed as a wet avalanche about 6 m wide. It carried the skier down the gully 65 vertical metres and then over a cliff of similar height. His body stopped against small trees on a scree slope. His partner reported the accident to the RCMP in Banff who relayed the report to the Banff Park Wardens. Using a rescuer suspended on a long line under a helicopter, wardens picked up the body at 18:57.

**Source:** Banff Park Warden Service

**Comment:** Once on the ridge, the skiers could not see the cliff below the gully due to the convex shape of the terrain. They chose to ski a steep gully late in the day when the snow was soft and "mushy."

# Nakiska Ski Area, Kananaskis Country

16 January 1988

### • slab avalanche involving snowmaking

At 09:30 on January 16th at the Nakiska Ski Area, two skiers entered the Bullshead run which was closed for snowmaking. The skiers continued in spite of warnings from the snowmaking staff. At an elevation of 2000 m, one skier triggered a 40 m-wide slab on a convex slope. He was carried 25 m into trees but was not injured. The 40 cm-thick slab started on old snow and stepped down to the ground. It ran a total distance of 100 m down the slope and through trees (Fig. 4.13).

On the run, 20 cm of faceted snow had been ski-packed in December but had been weakened by further cold temperatures. Snowmaking had deposited dense artificial snow on the weak base. For twenty-four hours prior to the accident, snowmaking deposited additional moist snow. On January 16th, the temperature measured 75 m below the accident site rose from an overnight low of -11.0°C to -6.2°C at 11:00.

**Source:** Nakiska Ski Area staff

**Comment:** The incident shows that machine-made snow can avalanche.

The skiers exposed themselves to a hazard by skiing a closed run. The skier could easily have been seriously injured by the hard slab avalanche which ran a further 75 m through trees.

*Fig. 4.13 Nakiska Ski Area, 88-01-16. S - survivor.*

# Standfast Creek, Selkirk Mountains

17 January 1988

- **one heli-ski guide killed**
- **fatal trauma from hitting trees**
- **75 cm slab on surface hoar**

| Date 1988 | Time | Max. Temp. (°C) | Min. Temp. (°C) | 24 h Snowfall (cm) | Snowpack Height (cm) | Wind (km/h) |
|---|---|---|---|---|---|---|
| Weather Conditions at Mt. Fidelity Elevation 1905 m, 20 km northeast of accident site | | | | | | |
| 01-10 | 0700 | -9 | -12 | 22 | 148 | 27 - S |
| 01-11 | 0700 | -7 | -12 | 6 | 144 | 32 - NW |
| 01-12 | 0700 | -8 | -11 | 10 | 150 | 26 - S |
| 01-13 | 0700 | -9 | -11 | 8 | 151 | 7 - S |
| 01-14 | 0700 | -6 | -9 | 25 | 163 | 6 - E |
| 01-15 | 0700 | -3 | -6 | 25 | 172 | 23 - S |
| 01-16 | 0700 | -6 | -9 | 13 | 174 | 4 - S |
| 01-17 | 0700 | -7 | -10 | 13 | 180 | 7 - S |

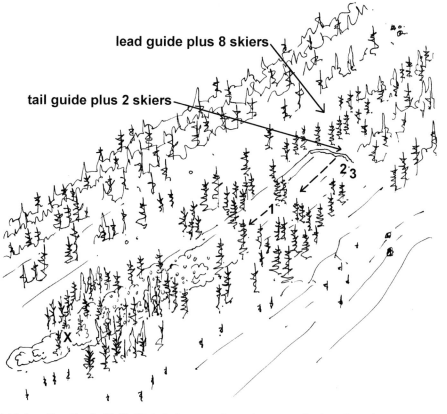

*Fig. 4.14 Standfast Creek, 88-01-17. 1, 2, 3 - approximate locations of tail guide and two slower skiers when avalanche started. X - deceased tail guide.*

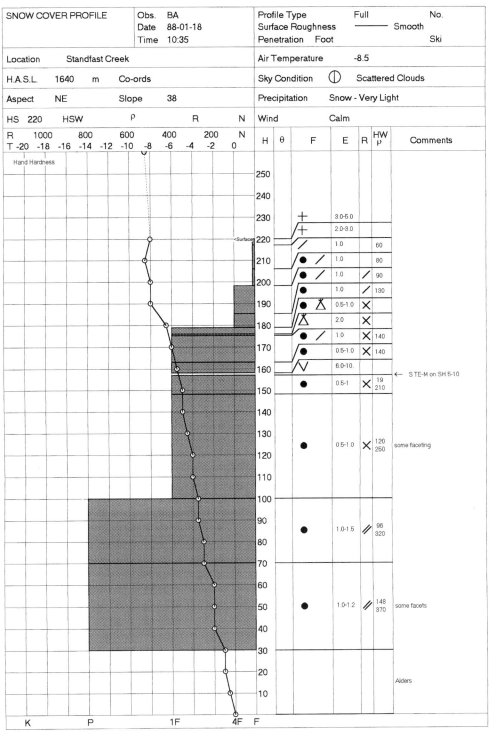

100 m from fracture line of accident avalanche. The surface hoar at 157-158 had collapsed in some areas of the pit. Shovel tests were performed on uncollapsed sections.

*Fig. 4.15 Profile observed near site of Standfast Creek avalanche on the day after the accident.*

During the first week of January, very little snow fell and surface hoar formed while the air temperature had ranged between -17°C and -10°C. Approximately 100 cm of snow fell during warmer temperatures in the week prior to the accident. On January 17th, a group of helicopter skiers were skiing in the east-facing slopes above Standfast Creek.

On the first run after lunch, the lead guide and eight skiers stopped at 1620 m on a small ridge. The tail guide and two slower skiers stopped above an open glade in the forest about 30 m to the side of the other skiers. The tail guide then descended over convex rolls in the glade and triggered a size 2.5 slab avalanche. One of the two skiers was caught near the edge of the avalanche and was able to ski to the side. The lead guide had heard a thumping sound and looked to see the tail guide carried 50 m by the avalanche and then out of sight behind trees (Fig. 4.14).

The lead guide organised the rescue. Although a transceiver search was initiated, searchers first spotted the tail guide's ski, then lower down near the toe of the deposit, his pack and boot. His head, buried 50 cm, was dug out within 7 minutes of the avalanche. CPR was started but stopped after 20 minutes when the victim was pronounced dead. Unfortunately, he had been pushed into trees by the avalanche and fatally injured.

The crown of the dry slab avalanche was 40 m wide and 75 cm thick. It was located at a convexity on a 35° slope. As shown in Fig. 4.15, the slab failed on a layer of surface hoar. It was a soft slab that ran about 350 m along the slope and through open forest.

**Comment:** Shovel shears on the surface hoar in the area ranged from *easy* to *hard*. At one site, the surface hoar did not fail consistently or smoothly. This variability is one factor that makes stability of slabs overlying surface hoar difficult to assess.

Avalanches can run in open forest. Sparse trees may do little to slow the avalanche but do increase the risk of traumatic injuries. Unfortunately, the trauma thwarted the very fast rescue.

---

# Crowfoot Pass, Banff National Park

7 February 1988

- **one backcountry skier killed**
- **no transceivers**
- **terrain trap**

Crowfoot Pass is a popular one-day ski tour that starts on the Icefields Parkway about 30 km northwest of the Lake Louise townsite. The pass can be reached from the valley bottom by following a broad ridge or a prominent gully.

On February 7th, twelve skiers left the Icefields Parkway to tour to Crowfoot Pass. Temperatures in the previous three days ranged between -12 and -3°C and very little snow had fallen. On the 7th, weather conditions were overcast with flurries. The air warmed to -5°C by mid-day.

Two skiers went ahead of the others, reaching the Pass first. When the main group arrived, the same two skiers began to descend on their own. At 13:30 while skiing down the gully, the first skier heard the second call out. Looking back, he could see only an avalanche deposit.

The first skier climbed back to the deposit and poked the surface for 10 minutes. Neither he nor his partner had avalanche transceivers. He then climbed back up the main group for help. All descended to the accident site. Nine people began to probe the deposit with skis and poles. Two skied out for additional help. At

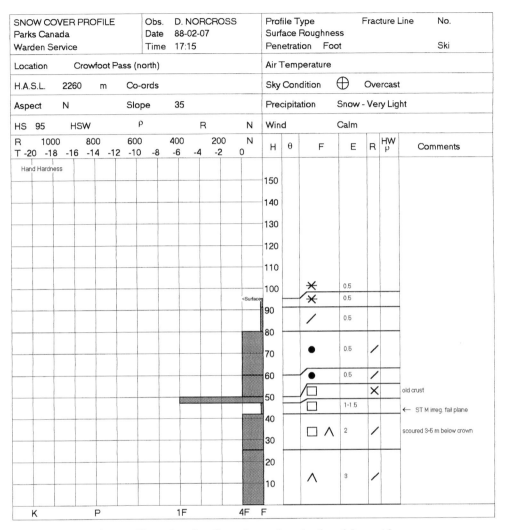

*Fig. 4.16 Fracture line profile at Crowfoot Pass observed on the day of the accident.*

14:15, the buried skier was located by probing under 1 m of snow. Five minutes of shovelling exposed the victim. The group cleared his airway and started CPR. Resuscitation efforts continued until 17:10 when the Park Wardens arrived.

As shown in Fig. 4.16, the slab failed on a layer of faceted crystals, just under a crust. This failure released a slab that averaged 40 cm in thickness and reached a maximum of 65 cm. The crown for the size 2 avalanche extended 80 m along the top of a 35° slope on the northwest-facing side of the gully at an elevation of 2255 m. The gully funnelled the avalanche into a deposit that reached 3 m in thickness (Fig. 4.17).

**Source:** Banff Park Warden Service

**Comment:** Transceivers would have sped up the search and improved the victim's odds of survival. Had the two skiers stayed with the main group, probing with nine people would have started sooner.

Gullies concentrate the avalanche forces and deposit and make it difficult or impossible to ski away from the avalanche.

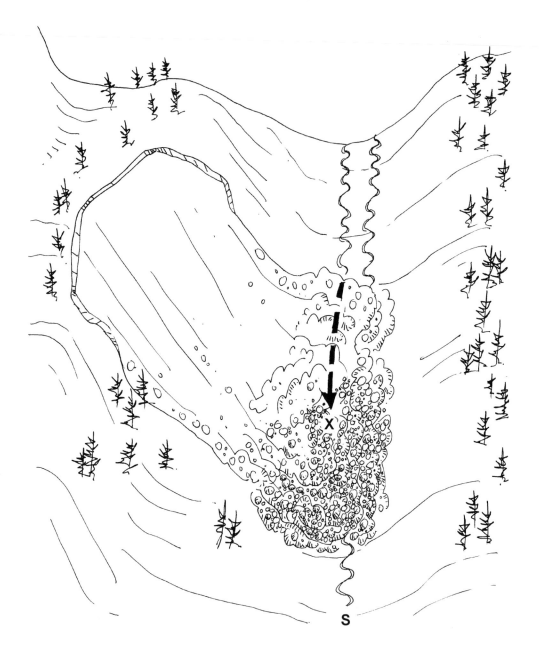

*Fig. 4.17 Crowfoot Pass, 88-02-07. S - survivor. X - deceased.*

# Sale Mountain, Selkirks

22 March 1988

- **two helicopter skiers buried, one killed**
- **long survival time**
- **storm snow sliding on surface hoar layer**

It was a little after noon on March 22nd when four skiers were dropped off by helicopter at the top of a ridge on Sale Mountain in the Selkirk Mountains of British Columbia. The slope they planned to ski dropped off the northeast side. The guide made his way onto the slope while the other three waited at a safe location on top. "I proceeded to ski the pitch [and] had done several turns…when I noticed the snow breaking up around me."

The sky was overcast, the temperature -3°C and a light wind was blowing from the southwest. About a week earlier there had been a period of mostly clear skies and overnight temperatures of -12°C which had built up surface hoar throughout the Selkirk Mountains. Then the following couple of days saw daytime temperatures climb above freezing with a moderate southwest wind. These latter conditions would have destroyed much of the surface hoar except in some isolated areas. During the past couple of days, it had snowed about 45 cm with moderate winds again coming from the southwest on the 20th. This would have substantially loaded lee, northeast aspects. As well, the temperatures over the past couple of days were conducive to slab development.

The slope the guide was on faced northeast and had a convex roll near the top with an angle of 40°.

As he skied over the convex roll, the snow fractured 10 m to each side of him. The depth of the slab was about 30 cm and released on a layer of graupel snow that had been deposited during the recent storm (Fig. 4.18). The time was 12:35. "I tried to out-ski the avalanche [by] going to my left. I lost my right ski, dropped my poles [and then] felt the snow roll over me". The size 1.5 avalanche carried him 25 m and buried him about 40 cm under the surface. "As I was being buried I was able to make an airspace around my mouth".

The three skiers at the top of the ridge saw the whole event and noted his last seen point. They then decided to send one skier down to do a transceiver search. Skier 2 skied down in the guide's tracks and onto the bed surface of the avalanche. He located the burial spot within two minutes and called to the other two to come down to help dig. Skiers 3 and 4 followed one at a time, skiing the same route. When Skier 4 reached the bed surface a second larger avalanche released. This time it released some 120 wide and 30 cm further down for a total depth of 60 cm, releasing on the surface hoar layer mentioned above. The time was 12:45. This avalanche, a size 2, ran down the slope for about 140 m, over the deposit of the first one, engulfing the three skiers and burying the guide even deeper. When the snow stopped moving, Skier 4 was buried up to her waist, Skier 2 was buried up to his chest, and the guide and Skier 3 were buried 1.2 m and 2 m down, respectively.

Skier 2 was able to extricate himself and, seeing that Skier 4 was all right, proceeded to search for the two buried skiers. He found the general location of Skier 3 but was unable to pinpoint her location, probably due to her burial depth. He removed the handle and used his ski pole as a probe but did not hit anything. He started digging, using only his hands because he did not have a shovel. The digging reduced the depth of Skier 3's burial and when he tried to probe again, he felt the skier. Digging by himself with just his hands proved too difficult and, needing help, he went over to Skier 4 who was unable to free herself because one of her skis was still attached to her boot. He managed to free her, but only after taking her foot out of her boot.

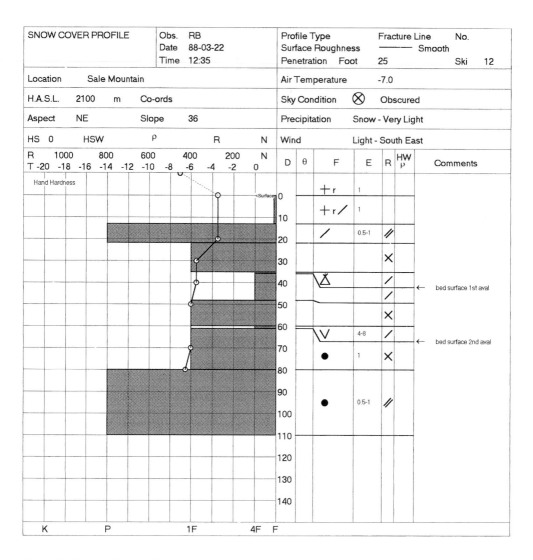

*Fig. 4.18 Fracture line profile observed at Sale Mountain on the day of the accident.*

Meanwhile, the helicopter pilot, not having seen nor heard from the group for 15 minutes, flew over the area and was able to determine that an avalanche had occurred and that two people were buried. He radioed the avalanche technician for the Ministry of Transportation and Highways in Revelstoke for rescue assistance and then flew over the accident site and dropped a radio to the two skiers on the surface. Skier 2, who had just freed himself, talked to the pilot and informed him of the situation. As they were talking, a guide working on Durrand Glacier about 13 km to the northwest, radioed for the pilot. The pilot asked him

if he would be available to aid in the rescue and on agreement flew over to pick him up. The helicopter and Guide 2 arrived back at the accident site at 13:20.

While Skier 2 continued digging, this time with a shovel (the guide had brought two), Guide 2 searched for Guide 1. He located and freed him in about 12 minutes (Fig. 4.19). He was in shock and hypothermic. He had been buried for at least 55 minutes. Guide 2 then went to help Skier 2 and together they uncovered Skier 3 by about 13:40. She had been buried for about the same amount of time but did not show any vital signs. A few minutes later

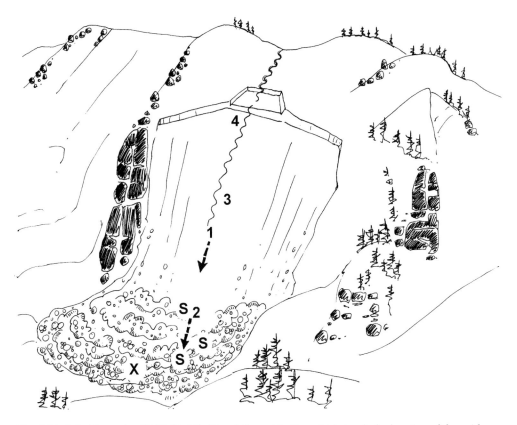

*Fig. 4.19 Sale Mountain, 88-03-22. All skiers followed in the guide's track. 1 - location of the guide when the first avalanche started. 2 - location of Skier 2, at the guide's burial spot, when the second avalanche started. 3, 4 - location of Skiers 3 and 4 when the second avalanche started. X - deceased. S - survivors. The fracture line of the initial avalanche can be seen above the crown of the main avalanche.*

the Highways rescue team from Revelstoke arrived at the scene and helped to extricate Skier 3. The helicopter then flew back to Revelstoke to deliver Guide 1 to the hospital and to pick up a stretcher, oxygen equipment and a doctor. At 13:54, Skier 3 was finally removed from the avalanche deposit and CPR was initiated. At 14:26 the doctor arrived and CPR was continued until 14:50 at which time the doctor pronounced her dead by asphyxiation.

**Comment:** The guide managed to survive a very long burial. A number of factors contributed to his good fortune. The air pocket he made just as the snow stopped moving and the unusually low density of the deposit allowed sufficient air to permeate through the snow so he could breathe. He was also able to hear all of the radio communication on his radio and therefore knew that help was coming soon.

# Whitetooth Mountain, near Golden, BC

3 April 1988

- **one out of bounds skier killed**
- **lack of awareness**

On their last run of the day three young skiers decided to head outside the Whitetooth ski area boundary. They skied past signs saying "Ski Area Boundary", "Closed" and "Warning. Avalanche area may be encountered if you ski outside designated ski runs". They skied 1 km across a forested slope to an area of sparse trees and then down to a cliff band they had skied in the morning. The slope angle here increased to 40°.

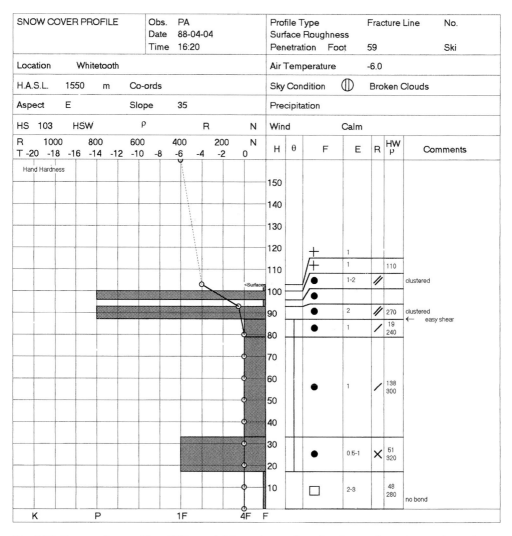

*Fig. 4.20 Fracture line profile at Whitetooth Mountain one day after the accident. Note isothermal (at 0°C) conditions from 80 cm to ground.*

During the previous few days the temperature had been warm and the radiation strong in the Whitetooth area near Golden, British Columbia. This had warmed up the snowpack to a point where all but the top 10 cm was isothermal at 0°C and quite weak. When they had skied the cliffs in the morning the skiers had started a small avalanche but it did not move far and did not scare them. The snowpack on the cliffs was only 103 cm deep with a poor bond at about 15 cm below the surface. It also had a thin crust at the surface formed by recent cooler temperatures (Fig. 4.20).

As they started skiing they broke through the thin crust and an avalanche released just below the third skier. The middle skier was moved a few meters but was able to grab a tree and hang on. The lowest skier was carried over a vertical part of the cliff. The wet slide ran through dense forest below the cliff and pushed the skier into a tree, burying him under about 1.2 m of dense snow. The avalanche probably initiated at the poor bond 15 cm below the surface and then, once in motion, caused the entire snowpack to come loose, sliding on the rocks of the cliff.

The other two skiers searched for ten minutes and found a broken ski but not the skier. They then went for help back at the ski area. A Parks Canada warden and his avalanche dog were the first to respond and arrived at the scene about one and a half hours after the avalanche had occurred. Once on the avalanche debris, the dog immediately indicated an area around a spruce tree. The warden probed the area and hit the victim at the base of the tree. He was quickly dug out but it was already too late. The skier had died from trauma as a result of his fall over the cliff and being pushed into the tree.

**Source:** Gord Peyto, Glacier National Park

**Comment:** A lack of awareness is often as dangerous as the avalanches themselves. Ski areas control their runs so they will not avalanche and when an area is closed, it is for good reason. Outside the area boundary none of the slopes are controlled and therefore become wilderness areas. Ski areas make it possible for people to get into areas they would otherwise not be able to access. However, ski areas can only do so much to prevent people from leaving their controlled environment. It is up to the individual to respect the signs.

# Garibaldi Provincial Park

2 January 1989

- **one out-of-bounds skier killed**
- **skiing above 75 m cliff**
- **60 cm of storm snow poorly bonded to an ice crust**

The northeast corner of Garibaldi Provincial Park, 125 km north of Vancouver, is accessible by skiers leaving the Blackcomb Ski Area boundary. At about 11:00, three local residents decided to ski Christmas Chute. Access was fairly easy, a 10 minute hike through some rock bands on Crystal Ridge, which divides Horstman Glacier from Blackcomb Glacier. When they saw that Christmas Chute had been

skied, they decided to ski an adjacent chute down to just above a 75 m cliff, then traverse back into Christmas Chute.

After two ski cuts at the top of the chute, two skiers remained above a small cliff band while one skier cut under it, out of sight of his partners. He triggered an avalanche on the 39° slope, called out and was carried 30 m down the slope and then over the 75 m cliff. The avalanche deposited 2 m of snow on top of him.

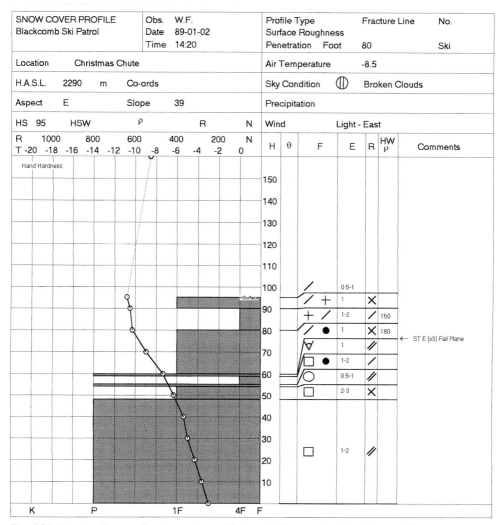

*Fig. 4.21 Fracture line profile observed near Christmas Chute on the day of the accident.*

Another skier who had witnessed the accident returned to the ski area to call for additional help.

The two skiers from the victim's group descended past the cliff band to the deposit where they used their transceivers to locate the victim's signal. After 20 minutes of digging they exposed the victim's hand. Further digging exposed the victim's head but the hole was not big enough for artificial respiration or CPR. A third person arrived and helped enlarge the hole sufficiently to begin CPR. Two heli-ski guides who had observed the rescue from the air arrived to assist, and the initial search leader from

Blackcomb Ski Patrol arrived half an hour after the accident. Five minutes later, two patrollers were slung onto the scene with defibrillator, cardiac monitor and doctor's pack. The victim was flown to the Whistler Medical Clinic at 12:25 where he was pronounced dead.

The initial slab for the size 3 dry slab avalanche was 100 m wide and 50 m long. The thickness at the fracture line varied from 20 to 180 cm. Sixty cm of storm snow had fallen in the two days before the accident. Strong winds from the southwest had moved additional snow into the northeast-facing start zone. The slab ran on a thin ice crust that had formed at the

end of the previous storm. Shovel shear tests done along with a fracture line profile after the accident showed *very easy* and *easy* shears on the thin ice crust.

**Source:** Blackcomb Ski Patrol

**Comment:** The avalanche hazard was rated as *high* on the day of the accident due to wind-loading and 60 cm of recent storm snow that was poorly bonded to an ice crust. The group chose to ski above a cliff.

This case demonstrates that proper rescue equipment and a quick response by rescuers may not be sufficient if the victim is fatally injured by the avalanche or deeply buried. Considerable time is required to dig a hole over 2 m deep in an avalanche deposit.

---

# Bella Vista, Monashee Mountains

15 March 1989

- **two helicopter skiers buried, one killed**
- **isolated weakness**

Four groups of heli-skiers had spent the morning of March 15th skiing a large slope above treeline in the Monashee Mountains of British Columbia. By the end of the morning the slope was completely tracked up and they started moving to a new location. As the last group was leaving they traversed across the slope, spread well apart.

There was a light wind, the sky was mostly cloudy and the temperature was -10.5°C.

The guide and three skiers crossed the slope safely. As the next three were on the slope, they triggered a size 2.5 avalanche. The fracture propagated around and above a large rock outcrop below which they were skiing, releasing an avalanche with a width of 120 m and a depth of about 90 cm. It ran about 600 m. The hard slab failed in a layer of deteriorating facets and slid on a thin, old rain crust (Fig. 4.22). This rain crust had been formed back in early February. All three skiers were carried down, one was partially buried and remained on a bench, but the other two were completely buried on another bench further down (Fig. 4.23). They were both under about 1 m of snow.

The guide told the remaining skiers to turn their transceivers to receive. He then quickly zigzagged across the debris to where he picked up a signal. Once located, the first victim was rapidly dug out. After being buried for only seven minutes he was unconscious, blue in the face and not breathing. However, after receiving a couple of air breaths from one of the rescuers, he was able to breath on his own again. The second victim was uncovered 17 minutes after the avalanche occurred, but he had died of trauma.

**Comment:** Some avalanches are hard to predict. It is unlikely for a slope to avalanche after being so tracked up. What this case demonstrates well is the variability of nature with the ever-present possibility of isolated weaknesses.

Minimising the number of people that are exposed to danger at any one time, through methods like proper spacing, can go a long way to reducing consequences.

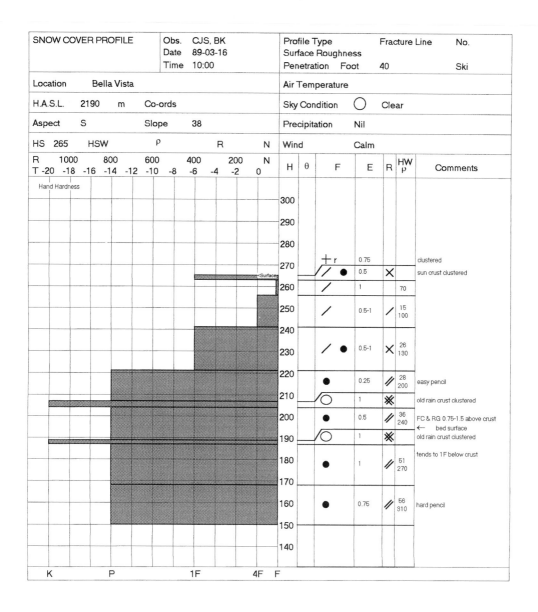

*Fig. 4.22 Fracture line profile observed at Bella Vista on the day after the accident.*

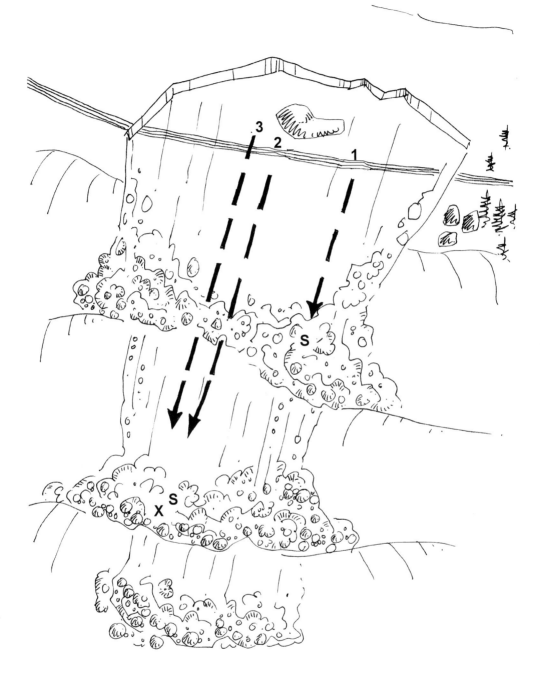

*Fig. 4.23 Bella Vista, 89-03-15. 1 to 3 - location of skiers when avalanche started. X - deceased. S - survivors.*

# Flute Mountain, near Whistler, BC

15 March 1989

- **three out of bounds skiers buried, one killed**
- **terrain trap**

Four skiers took the chair lift up to the top of Whistler Mountain, in the Coast Mountains of British Columbia. From there they traversed over to Flute Mountain, outside the ski area boundary, and climbed to the top of an untracked slope. They had a video camera along and were filming each other skiing off the cornice and down through the fresh powder snow. For the third run the camera man positioned himself on the uphill side of a small moraine that ran along the bottom of the slope.

A *high* avalanche danger for the backcountry had been posted that day but it had been ignored by the four skiers.

With the camera running, two of the skiers jumped off the cornice at the same time. When they landed, their impact released a 250 m-wide slab. It averaged 135 cm in thickness and slid on an old crust. It travelled 200 m down the slope and piled up against the moraine, burying the camera man under 4 m of snow. The two skiers who triggered the avalanche were also engulfed in the moving snow and ended up buried under 60 cm.

Some people in the area witnessed the entire avalanche and members of the Whistler Ski Patrol saw the avalanche just as it was ending. When the snow stopped moving they could see pieces of clothing sticking out above the snow. The two skiers were soon uncovered and they suffered only minor bruises. The patrollers searched the deposit with transceivers, avalanche dog and probes, locating the camera man under the great depth of snow. About a dozen people frantically dug a huge hole in order to get down to him. It was, however, too late. A doctor at the scene pronounced him dead on site.

**Source:** Whistler Ski Patrol

**Comment:** Recognising dangerous terrain features is key for safe travel in the backcountry and must be practised constantly. In this case the avalanche would probably not have been as deadly if the snow had not piled up against the moraine the camera man was on. He would have been better off to position himself on the crest of the moraine instead of on the uphill side.

# Wawa Bowl, Banff National Park

6 January 1990

- **one out-of-bounds snowboarder killed**
- **no transceivers, probes or shovels**

| | | Weather Conditions at Sunshine Ski Village Elevation 2145 m, 1.5 km SE of accident site | | | | |
|---|---|---|---|---|---|---|
| Date 1990 | Time | Max. Temp. (°C) | Min. Temp. (°C) | Precip. (mm) | Snowpack Height (cm) | Wind (km/h) |
| 01-04 | 1500 | -8 | -10 | 2 | 131 | 10 - W |
| 01-05 | 0800 | -8 | -11 | 0 | 130 | 18 - SW |
| 01-05 | 1500 | -6 | -9 | 1 | 128 | 39 - SW |
| 01-06 | 0800 | -4 | -6 | 9 | 133 | 37 - SW |
| 01-06 | 1500 | -6 | -7 | 1 | 133 | 40 - SW |

A snowboarder and two skiers took the last ride up the Wawa T-bar at the Sunshine Ski Area on January 6th. They left the ski area and traversed to Wawa Bowl. The snowboarder used snowshoes and carried his board.

In Banff National Park the early season snowpack had been relatively stable until a surface hoar layer was buried by snowfall on December 16th. In the days before the accident, southwest winds picked up fresh snow and deposited slabs in lee slopes such as Wawa Bowl.

When they reached the bowl, the snowboarder put his board on his feet and snowshoes on his back. All three entered the bowl at the same time and triggered a 70 cm-thick slab. The snowboarder who was farthest down the slope was buried face down under 2 m of snow. The board on his feet and the snowshoes on his back had probably acted as anchors, dragging him deeper into the snow. The two skiers lost their skis and were partly buried. After searching briefly for the snowboarder, the two skiers walked back to the ski area to get help. Without their skis to speed the descent, they reported the accident 2 hours after the avalanche. It was too dark for a helicopter.

Ski area staff responded with a snowcat and snowmobiles. Parks Canada Wardens and three dog handlers were dispatched. The snowcat's headlights lit the slope. After the visual search an organised probe line started at 20:16. The dog and handler from Banff found the victim under 2 m of snow, almost 5 hours after the avalanche. He had suffocated. Twenty rescuers worked on the search.

The 30 m wide dry slab failed on a layer of facets believed to be metamorphosed surface hoar buried on December 16th. The crown, which reached a maximum thickness of 130 cm, was just below the cornice at 2400 m on the northeast-facing slope.

**Source:** Banff Park Warden Service

**Comment:** The group did not assess the snow stability and entered the slope together. They had no transceivers, shovels or probes.

The snowboard on his feet and the snowshoes on his back probably contributed to the snowboarder's deep burial. This is the earliest report of a snowboarder killed by an avalanche in Canada.

A fatal accident also occurred on this slope on 27 December 1984 (Fig. 4.1).

# Chester Lake, Kananaskis Country

7 January 1990

- **buried dog tunneled 180 cm to surface over 18-20 hours**

At mid day on January 7th, a man and his golden retriever were traversing a slope about 60 m from the west end of Chester Lake when they triggered a class 2 slab avalanche. The man was carried a short distance and buried to his waist. Two skiers observed the slide and came to help the man dig himself out. There was no sign of the dog. They probed for 20 minutes without success. "I thought for sure she was dead". The man descended to the Smith-Dorian road where he contacted rangers from Lougheed Provincial Park.

When Kananaskis Country staff returned the next day to search for the dog's body, they found the dog, barking frantically. A 180 cm tunnel led diagonally upwards from where the dog had been buried, 110 cm down, to the surface. She had emerged near the hole where her master had been partly buried. Apparently, the dog tunnelled in the direction she was facing, leaving an icy tunnel 35 cm in diameter. The dog's paws were so iced she could barely walk.

Rescuers believe the dog had tunnelled for 18-20 hours, reaching the surface only hours before they arrived. "There were no snowflakes on the footprints around the hole, and we had 6 cm of fresh snow overnight." One of the rescuers carried the dog to the trailhead in his pack.

**Source:** George Field, Kananaskis Country

**Comment:** People buried in avalanches usually report being unable to move. However, the deposit from this small avalanche allowed the dog to dig *and breathe for 18-20 hours*. "It was probably a mix of blocks and light snow that left some airspace."

At least one manufacturer of avalanche transceivers sells a smaller unit that transmits on a secondary frequency. After locating people on the primary frequency, searchers with the appropriate transceivers can switch their units to receive on the secondary frequency and search for dogs, snowmobiles, skis or any item to which the smaller transmitters have been attached.

*Fig. 4.24  Chester Lake. Dog being evacuated after tunnelling through avalanche deposit to surface. Jock Richardson photo.*

# Sand Creek, Southern Rockies

28 January 1990

- **one snow-cat skier killed**
- **recent heavy snowfall**
- **buried surface hoar**

| Date 1990 | Time | Max. Temp. (°C) | Min. Temp. (°C) | Snowfall (cm) | Storm Snow (cm) | Snowpack Height (cm) |
|---|---|---|---|---|---|---|
| 01-21 | 1555 | -2.5 | -5.5 | 0 | 0 | 186 |
| 01-22 | 0805 | -2.5 | -3.5 | 35 | 35 | 223 |
| 01-22 | 1600 | -2.5 | -3.0 | 17 | 50 | 239 |
| 01-23 | 0745 | -3.0 | -6.0 | 12 | 59 Cl | 245 |
| 01-23 | 1535 | -5.0 | -6.0 | 0.1 | 0.1 | 243 |
| 01-24 | 0815 | -5.0 | -10.0 | 0 | 0 | 232 |
| 01-24 | 1550 | -7.0 | -10.5 | 0.1 | 0.1 | 232 |
| 01-25 | 0820 | -5.0 | -7.0 | 10 | 10 | 240 |
| 01-25 | 1540 | -3.5 | -5.5 | 9 | 16 | 249 |
| 01-26 | 0800 | -3.0 | -9.0 | 4 | 19 | 250 |
| 01-26 | 1600 | -7.0 | -10.0 | 0 | 17 Cl | 248 |
| 01-27 | 0810 | -9.0 | -12.5 | 0.1 | 0.1 | 246 |
| 01-27 | 1605 | -8.0 | -10.0 | 25 | 27 | 274 |
| 01-28 | 0800 | -6.5 | -9.0 | 25 | 45 | 287 |
| 01-28 | 1310 | - | - | 6 | 48 | 290 |

Weather Conditions at Fernie Snow Valley
Elevation 1645 m, 8.5 km ESE of accident site

The slopes of the Lizard Range above Sand Creek lie immediately east of the Kootenay Valley near Cranbrook, BC and west of Fernie, BC. The area attracts ski tourers as well as groups of skiers carried up the slopes by snow-cats.

After a period of clear weather, snow started to fall on January 21st, burying a layer of surface hoar in many areas of BC. From the 21st to the 28th, over 140 cm of snow fell at 1645 m in the Fernie Snow Valley Ski Area, which is just east of the crest of the Lizard Range. The Sand Creek area to the west received approximately half as much snow, including 15 cm and 16 cm of snow on the mornings of 27th and 28th. Light winds and no avalanches were observed in the Sand Creek area.

On January 28th, a group of 11 cat skiers and four guides was skiing 60-70 cm of snow that had fallen in the previous week. It was overcast and snowing lightly. On the third run in the area, three skiers were caught in an avalanche that split and flowed into two gullies. After counting the survivors, they realised that two skiers were missing and that one was partly buried and uninjured. They began a transceiver search of the 4000 m² deposit. One skier was found alive and uninjured on the upper part of one arm of the deposit, buried under 70 cm of snow. The other victim was found in the lower half of the second gully, under 2.5 m of snow. He was dug out—unresponsive—35 minutes after the avalanche. Rescuers began and continued CPR while he was transported to Cranbrook Hospital where he was declared dead. The autopsy found that he had suffocated.

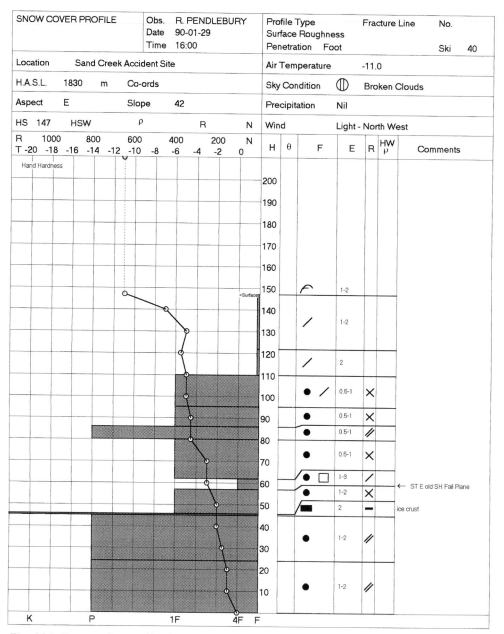

*Fig. 4.25 Fracture line profile observed at the site of the Sand Creek accident on the day after the accident.*

The size 3 slab avalanche started at 1830 m, approximately 50 m below the ridge where the slope is open and treeless. Although much of the start zone is 35°, the crown was located on a convexity where the inclination reached 42°. The slab averaged 60 cm in thickness and was 80 m wide. It failed on a layer of surface hoar about 60 cm above the ground (Fig. 4.25). The deposit terminated in gullies at 1675 m where it reached 3 m in depth (Fig. 4.26).

**Source:** Rod Pendlebury and Chris Stethem

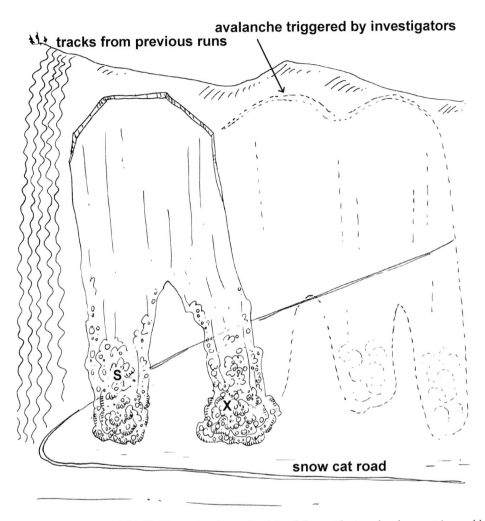

*Fig. 4.26 Sand Creek, 90-01-28. The avalanche to the right of the accident avalanche was triggered by investigators on the day after the accident.*

**Comment:** The buried surface hoar layer was present in the region. However, the layer was not identified in the area prior to the accident.

As additional snow layers are added to the snowpack, buried surface hoar often gives little or no advance warning that it is being critically overloaded. However, four more large avalanche deposits were observed in the area the day after the accident, indicating that the load had become critical. Investigators triggered one of these avalanches.

Settlement of storm snow is generally associated with less frequent avalanching, and the guides felt that settlement during the storm was good. However, in the case of persistent weak layers such as surface hoar, settlement of the overlying slab often means that any fractures in the persistent weak layer tend to propagate farther. In such cases, avalanches often become less frequent but those that release on the persistent weak layer are potentially larger. Consequently, monitoring persistent weak layers is important to avalanche forecasting.

The gullies below the slope constituted terrain traps since they funnelled the avalanche into deep deposits. The numerous shovellers probably contributed to the live recovery of one of the two buried victims.

# Battleship Mountain, Kokanee Glacier Park

30 January 1990

- **two backcountry skiers killed**
- **convex roll**
- **storm snow on surface hoar**

On the morning of the 30th two skiers separated from a larger group to go skiing on their own. They made their way up a slope on the northern side of Battleship Mountain in Kokanee Glacier Park, British Columbia. They reached the top a little before noon.

The sky was overcast and very light snow was falling. It had been storming for the preceding nine days and they had not been able to fly into the hut until the previous day due to the moderate snowfall and strong winds. Back in mid-January a clear period had produced a surface hoar layer that was now buried by about 70 cm of storm snow. Several avalanches had been seen the day before while flying in, on both east and west aspects.

As this accident was unwitnessed, it is not known exactly what happened. What is apparent is that the two skiers entered the slope from the top and both were on the slope when it slid. The crown of the avalanche was just below a convex roll and had an estimated width of 350 m and a depth of 70 cm. It probably slid on the surface hoar layer at the interface with the old snow. The two skiers were caught in the size 3 avalanche and buried near the base of the slope, one under 1.3 m of snow and the other under 2.5 m.

Some time after lunch some members of the original group noticed the new fracture line and the tracks leading into it. They initiated a rescue and the park ranger radioed for help from the police. Using transceivers, the rescuers were able to quickly locate the two skiers. They dug them out as fast as they could and then administered CPR, but the victims had already been buried for over two hours and had died of suffocation.

**Source:** Kevin Giles, Kokanee Glacier Mountaineering and Dave Smith, BC Ministry of Transportation and Highways

**Comment:** Right after a storm, especially one of this magnitude, is a time to be very cautious. The storm snow needs time to settle and strengthen, and if a buried weak layer is suspected, the strength of that layer needs to be assessed carefully. If a slope is suspect, either it should be avoided altogether or, if that is not an option, it should be skied one at a time while the other skiers are watching from a safe location.

# Healy Creek Trail, Banff National Park

11 February 1990

- **four backcountry skiers killed**
- *extreme* **avalanche hazard**
- **large well-organised rescue**

| | | Weather Conditions at Sunshine Ski Village | | | | | | |
|---|---|---|---|---|---|---|---|---|
| | | Elevation 2145 m, 3 km SE of accident site | | | | | | |
| Date 1990 | Time | Max. Temp. (°C) | Min. Temp. (°C) | Precip. (cm/h) | Snowfall (cm) | Snow Density (kg/m³) | Total Snowpack (cm) | Wind (km/h) |
| 02-09 | 1500 | -8 | -14 | S 1 | 4 | 55 | 193 | 34 - SW |
| 02-10 | 0730 | -5 | -8 | S 1 | 26 | 63 | 211 | 23 - SW |
| 02-10 | 1500 | -4 | -6 | S 1 | 10 | 80 | 218 | 13 - W |
| 02-11 | 0730 | -3 | -5 | S 2 | 29 | 111 | 238 | 26 - SW[1] |
| 02-11 | 1200 | - | - | S 2 | - | - | - | 24 - S[1] |

[1] wind at observation site; others are ridgetop winds.

On February 11th, five skiers left the Bourgeau Trailhead to ski tour towards Healy Pass. One skier lagged behind the other four and lost sight of them about half an hour up the trail. About 12:15 she heard a noise like an avalanche and continued across the foot bridge which is about 2 km up the trail. By 13:00, it was snowing heavily and visibility was poor. She turned around. While returning to the trailhead she mentioned to a party of two headed up the trail that her four friends were further up the trail.

Two large avalanche paths cross the Healy Creek trail about 3.5 and 4 km from the trailhead (Fig. 4.27). Avalanches from these paths do not frequently run far enough to cross the trail. However, conditions were exceptional. In the previous three days, 76 cm of snow had fallen at Sunshine Ski Village, 3 km to the southeast. As temperatures had warmed during the storm, the density had increased, building a slab of relatively dense snow over lighter layers.

Two other groups had gone up the trail earlier in the day, crossing the two avalanche paths at about 11:30. On their way down, they noticed a huge avalanche deposit across the trail at the second slide path. When they encountered the party of two at about 14:00, they real-ised the four skiers from the party of five might be buried. They quickly searched the deposit and returned to the trailhead to report the accident.

The avalanche in the second path started 350 m above the trail at a corniced ridge (elevation 2350 m) at the top of a southeast-facing bowl. The crown averaged 1.5 m in thickness and reached a maximum of 4 m. From the 35° slope below the cornice, the avalanche picked up additional snow on the way down. It ran across the creek and 70 m up the other side. The deposit included large blocks of hard snow from the cornice. The deposit was 185 m wide where it crossed the trail. Although the established slide path was only 118 m wide at the trail, the deposit extended into mature timber 20 m to the east and 47 m to the west of the path. Apparently the four skiers were having lunch—in what would normally be considered a safe place—when the avalanche ran through the mature forest to the west of the path, snapping trees up to 15 cm in diameter. Avalanches of this size are expected in this path only once every 30-50 years.

Once they verified that four people were indeed missing, Banff Park Wardens initiated a full scale search at 16:40. Dogmasters and helicopters were dispatched. Most rescuers

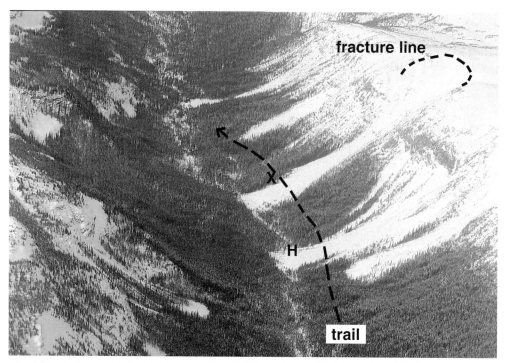

*Fig. 4.27 Healy Creek, 90-02-11. X - location of all four victims. H - heli-pad used during rescue. Bruce Jamieson photo.*

started up the trail on skis. Others began making a snowmobile trail up from the trailhead. A helicopter dropped the first dog and master off at the large deposit in the second path, and then continued flying up the valley searching for the skiers. When none were seen, the helicopter began moving rescue teams to the site until dark. The snowmobile trail reached the site at 19:00, after which teams were able to reach the site by snowmobile. Thirty searchers worked until 22:40 without success.

On the morning of February 12th, the search resumed at 07:00. Avalanche dog teams, probers and shovellers travelled to the site by snowmobile since visibility did not permit flying. Avalanche dogs were unable to find human scents, probably because of the strong smell from the many smashed conifers in the deposit. Rescuers also set up a helicopter pad and campsite for shelter on the first avalanche path several hundred metres to the east of the accident site.

The flurries on the morning of the 12th were followed by clearing and cooling. When visibility improved, helicopters bombed the slide paths above the Sunshine road, releasing two large avalanches that blocked the road for four hours. By evening the air temperature reached -24°C. Rescuers returned to Banff by 20:00.

At 07:00 on February 13th, a Level IV Rescue response began. Searchers from Banff, Jasper, Kootenay, Waterton and Glacier National Parks and Kananaskis Country formed the probe teams. Four dog teams searched the deposit.

At 08:30 the start zones of the two Healy Creek avalanche paths were bombed from helicopters to remove any remaining unstable snow. The avalanche in the first path covered the helicopter pad and ran to the creek. Improved visibility and this stabilization of the snow above the helicopter pad allowed rescuers to fly to and from the site for the remainder of the rescue. Two helicopters and fifty people worked in the field in temperatures below -30°C. Teams

of searchers rotated to the camp for warming and food. Two searchers froze their toes and were evacuated.

Based on indications from search dogs, probers searched the toe of the deposit. At 10:00 the first victim was located in the forest west of the open path. The dog may have been assisted by the victim's ski tip which was just below the surface. Several articles were found near the first victim and by noon all of the probers were deployed in the forest near the location of the first victim. A short distance away, the second victim was found. Searchers returned to Banff at dusk.

Searchers returned to the scene on the morning of the 14th. Fortunately, the air temperature had warmed to -15°C. At 10:20 a search dog indicated a third possible victim. Shovelling at this site located the two remaining victims. All victims were found dead, 1.5 to 1.8 m below the surface. The avalanche had pushed them 8 to 18 m through trees below the trail where they were having lunch.

**Source:** Banff Park Warden Service

**Comment:** The skiers stopped in mature timber—which is usually considered a safe place to stop. However, one day before the accident, the avalanche hazard in the Sunshine and Assiniboine area was high. The bulletin stated "snowfalls of up to 40 cm have fallen along the continental divide in the last 24 hours. Should heavy snowfalls forecast for Sunday materialise, the avalanche hazard will approach extreme in most areas of the park." The heavy snowfalls on Sunday February 11th contributed to a very large avalanche that ran wider than usual. During extreme avalanche hazard, areas near avalanche terrain that are usually safe may not be.

The surviving member of the party was not aware if anyone in the group had obtained the avalanche bulletin before the trip.

Transceivers would not have helped the victims but would probably have made searching much faster.

The rescue effort was large and well organised. It involved personnel from five national parks, Sunshine Ski Village, the RCMP, Kananaskis Country, a helicopter company and an ambulance service. Rescuers worked in cold temperatures and on a hard avalanche deposit. Press conferences were held at specific times. Several relatives of the victims were flown over the accident site.

The strong smell from the broken conifers limited the effectiveness of the dogs, especially in the first two days of searching. Searchers believe that holes probed in the frozen deposit during the early stages of the search allowed the scent to reach the surface, facilitating subsequent searching by dogs.

# Rummel Col, Peter Lougheed Provincial Park

20 January 1991

- **one backcountry skier partially buried**
- **one completely buried and killed**
- **hard slab failing on faceted layer**

Three skiers left the trailhead at 11:30 on January 20th and skied up to Rummel Lake in Kananaskis Country, Alberta, reaching it by 13:30. They then carried on past the lake, following tracks from an earlier party towards a col to the northwest. One of the skiers decided she did not want to do any telemark skiing and turned around and went back down to the lake. The other two continued on, breaking out of the trees at 14:10. They discussed the avalanche danger and identified a large cornice as being a threat to the other side of the valley but considered their side to be relatively safe. They decided to go just a little further, climbing up towards a group of trees some 40 m directly above them. This would be their turn-around point. The lead skier made two switchbacks to ascend to the group of trees and only had about 10 m to go. He was 7 m in front of the second skier.

A high avalanche danger had been posted for the day. Faceting in the middle of the snowpack was the major weakness. The upper snowpack instability had resulted in many large natural avalanches over the past few days and the danger was increasing. Skiers were cautioned to stay off steep and/or wind-loaded slopes on all aspects.

*"The avalanche came with no warning...we were immediately thrown to our sides and no chance to ski off the slope. The initial size of the avalanche was small, only a square slab about 15 m to a side. This slab broke up between [the lead skier] and I, and he sped into the trees below and disappeared. The slab I was on missed the trees and carried me 50 m down slope and began to slow down. At that point I thought the avalanche was over. However, this small slide triggered the rest of the slope, and I heard a loud crack and looked over my shoulder to see the entire wall of the valley above*

*begin to move. Immediately afterward the slab I was on picked up speed again and then disintegrated. I was lying on my back and using my arms to try to swim upright. My head remained above the snow during the entire slide."*

The avalanche fracture propagated right up to the cornice at the col. Its width was 115 m and its depth varied greatly, averaging 80 cm. The snow had failed at the base of a weak faceted layer (Fig. 4.28). The avalanche carried the two skiers about 100 m before it stopped. One was partially buried but otherwise unhurt while the other was buried under 70 cm of snow. The partially buried skier called out for his friend while he was digging himself out but heard no reply. It took 5 minutes to free himself. The time was then 14:25.

Four skiers, meanwhile, were skiing up a slope a bit further to the west and witnessed the avalanche. They skied down to the slide area and assisted the partially buried skier. After determining that the other skier must be buried and that he was not wearing a transceiver, they formed a coarse probe line while one of them skied out for help. They used skis and ski poles to probe.

Upon reaching the trailhead the skier going for help notified the park rangers, who immediately put their avalanche rescue plan into effect. Two rangers and this skier were the first to respond; they flew into the site by helicopter, arriving at about 15:42. More flights immediately followed with other park rangers and Banff National Park dog master.

With the additional personnel and proper avalanche probes on hand, a larger probe line was established and at 16:45 one of the probers located the victim 9 m uphill from the toe of the avalanche debris. He was quickly uncovered but did not show any vital signs so

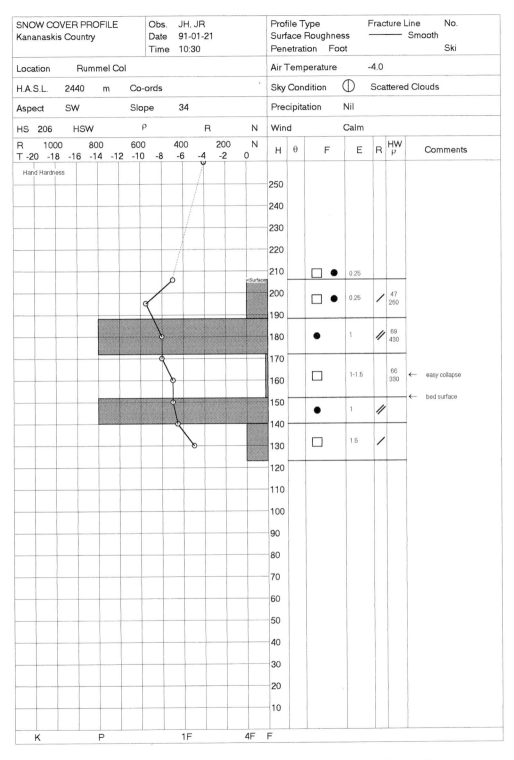

*Fig. 4.28  Fracture line profile observed at Rummel Col one day after the accident.*

*Fig. 4.29 Rummel Col, 91-01-20. 1, 2 - location of skiers when avalanche started.*
*X - deceased. S - survivor. Note crown extending from below col to shallower, windward*
*slopes in upper right of picture. The fracture probably propagated from a shallow point*
*around the trees. George Field photo.*

*Fig. 4.30 Rummel Col, 91-01-20. Slab thickness can be clearly seen to become shallower towards upper left of picture. George Field photo.*

CPR was initiated. A helicopter then slung the victim and the person administering CPR out to a nearby helipad. A helicopter ambulance arrived simultaneously and the doctor on board declared the victim deceased.

**Source:** George Field, Kananaskis Country

**Comment:** Much effort goes into preparing backcountry avalanche bulletins. They contain valuable information on snow stability and avalanche danger. Before heading out into the backcountry, access the bulletin most particular to your intended destination and choose terrain accordingly.

Organised professional rescue personnel will rarely arrive in time to find a buried victim alive. It is up to the accident party to rescue any member of their party that is caught. Had the two skiers been wearing avalanche transceivers, there would have been a good chance that the surviving skier, or the four from the other party, may have found his friend in time.

Following the tracks from an earlier group that morning may have lured this unfortunate party into believing they were still in safe terrain.

---

# East Col Blackcomb Glacier

9 April 1991

- **one out-of-bounds skier killed**
- **two people exposed at same time**
- **only one shovel**

On April 9th, the morning after a fresh snowfall, many ski tourers left the Blackcomb Ski Area. Two skiers ascended towards the col east of the Blackcomb Glacier, about 10 m above the track many others had used. The weather remained unsettled, with patches of fog and flurries.

A 40 km/h wind from the southeast continued to move additional snow from the recent storm onto lee slopes, including the west-facing slope that the out-of-bounds skiers were traversing. Similar slopes inside the ski area had been stabilized with explosives.

On the traverse they triggered a slab that extended 30 m above them. Both were carried down-slope and the first was completely buried. The second skier had injured a knee and was partly buried. It took 15 minutes to dig himself out since he did not have a shovel. He found his partner's ski sticking out of the snow and began to dig. Once he exposed his partner's pack, he removed the shovel from the pack

and continued to dig. About 50 minutes after the avalanche, he uncovered his partner who was buried head down and had suffocated.

The accident could not be seen from the ski area because of fog. This is unfortunate because the ski patrol were working with a helicopter, helping an injured skier lower on the mountain. They recovered the avalanche victim's body after being called to the accident site.

The size 2 avalanche started as a 50 m-wide slab. Its thickness averaged 50 cm but reached a maximum of 130 cm. As shown on the fracture line profile (Fig. 4.32), a slab of decomposed and fragmented grains from recent storms slid on a weak layer below a thin ice layer.

**Source:** Blackcomb Ski Patrol

**Comment:** The lure of untracked snow outside ski areas attracts many skiers, some of whom are not adequately prepared for backcountry skiing. The second skier did not have a shovel. Had the two skiers been further spaced apart, only one might have been caught.

*Fig. 4.31 East Col Blackcomb Glacier, 91-04-09. Accident party took higher traverse and may have triggered the avalanche in weaker snow near the rocks exposed by the avalanche. X - deceased. Wayne Flann photo.*

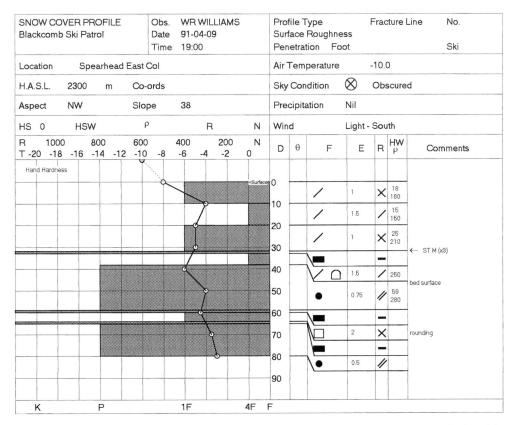

*Fig. 4.32 Fracture line profile observed at East Col Blackcomb Glacier (Spearhead Col) on the day of the accident.*

These skiers were caught while many others on the lower traverse did not trigger the slab. Their higher track was directed at a rock that was uncovered by the avalanche. The avalanche may have been triggered from shallower, weaker snow that often surrounds buried rocks (Logan, 1993).

---

# Mt. Strachan, West Vancouver

19 December 1992

- **one out-of-bounds skier killed**
- **no transceivers**

Two skiers left the Cypress Bowl Ski Area on Mt. Strachan to ski a steep northeast-facing bowl above Australian Gully. In the preceding few days, 50 cm of snow had fallen in the area. An avalanche released above the two skiers when the first skier was getting up from a fall. The second skier was buried to his neck against a tree, but was able to free himself. The first skier was carried further down into difficult terrain. Searchers spent two days looking for him but their efforts were hindered by an additional 50 cm of snow. A subsequent search with dogs was also unsuccessful. The body of the skier was found over five months later, on May 28th.

The size 2.5 avalanche started on a 40° slope at an elevation of 1370 m. The 50 cm-thick soft slab released 250 m wide. It failed on a surface hoar layer and slid on an icy crust.

**Source:** Cypress Bowl Ski Patrol, North Shore Search and Rescue, and Peter Schaerer

**Comment:** Snow stability outside ski areas is often very different from the stability on controlled runs within ski areas. The onus is on out-of-bounds skiers to assess the snow stability and choose appropriate terrain.

The two skiers were not equipped with transceivers nor prepared for self rescue.

# Parker's Ridge, Banff National Park

25 December 1992

- **one backcountry skier killed**
- **wind-loaded slope**
- **route selection**

Parker's Ridge is a popular area for backcountry skiing, especially early in the winter. The north- and east-facing slopes are located on the west side of the Icefield's Parkway, near the Hilda Creek Hostel about half way between Lake Louise and Jasper. However, many of the popular slopes are often wind-affected.

Two skiers were returning to the hostel from the ridge at 13:30 on December 25th. While traversing the lower third of a large wind-loaded

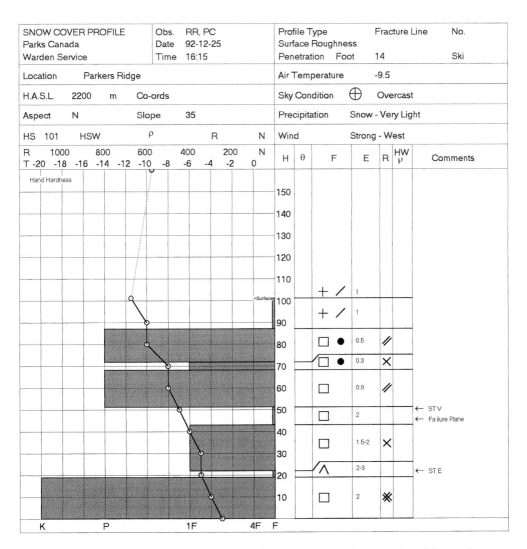

Fig. 4.33 Fracture line profile observed at the Parkers Ridge avalanche on the day of the accident.

slope south of the Hilda Creek Hostel, they triggered a slab and were both caught in the avalanche. One skier was buried but reached his hand almost to the surface as the avalanche stopped. He made a hole with his arm and then enlarged it to clear the snow from his face.

A third person who had witnessed the slide from the hostel hurried to the deposit and helped dig the man out. One hundred metres away, they found the second skier's legs on the surface of the deposit. They dug her out of the snow about 30 minutes after the avalanche but she had died.

The size 3 avalanche failed on a layer of 2 mm faceted crystals. The shovel test resulted in a *very easy* shear on this weak layer.

**Source:** Jasper Park Warden Service

**Comment:** The skiers chose to traverse a wind-loaded slope rather than skirting along the bottom of the runout. Avoiding the slope would have taken five minutes longer.

If the skiers had skied the slope one at a time, at most one person would have been caught, allowing a faster search.

---

# Mt. Albreda, Northern Monashees

16 March 1993

- **one helicopter skier caught under apparently stable conditions**

| | Weather Conditions at Mt. St. Anne | | | | |
| --- | --- | --- | --- | --- | --- |
| | Elevation 1900 m, 32 km SSE of accident site | | | | |
| Date 1993 | Time | Max. Temp. (°C) | Min. Temp. (°C) | Precip. (mm) | Wind (km/h) |
| 03-13 | 0530 | 0.6 | -12.0 | 0 | 28 - S |
| 03-14 | 0530 | -1.7 | -7.3 | 0 | 33 - S |
| 03-15 | 0530 | -4.5 | -14.4 | 32.0 | 34 - N |
| 03-16 | 0530 | -13.8 | -19.3 | 0 | 16 - N |
| 03-17 | 0530 | -6.3 | -19.6 | 0 | 12 - NE |
| 03-18 | 0530 | -5.3 | -11.9 | 11.4 | 21 - S |

On March 13th and 16th the height of the snowpack was 181 and 190 cm, respectively.

In the winter of 1992-93, snowfall was well below average throughout the North Columbia Mountains. Widespread surface hoar layers were buried on January 19th and February 10th causing persistent weak layers in the snowpack. However, no avalanche activity was reported in the area on the January 19th surface hoar layer after January 26th, nor on the February 10th layer after March 1st. On the afternoon and evening of March 14th, 32 mm of water fell as 40 cm of snow at Mt. St. Anne. As the temperature dropped, the wind shifted and blew from the north. This storm snow released as slabs up to 30 cm thick on March 14th and 15th. Avalanches from this storm did not step down to either of the surface hoar layers.

On March 16th, a group of four helicopter skiers and their guide skied several runs on the north slopes of Mt. Albreda. Each run was to the west of their previous tracks. On their third run down, the second skier after the guide triggered a 1 m-thick slab, 30 m wide. The size 2 avalanche carried the skier 50 m down-slope. He stopped, uninjured, near a few trees on the surface of the deposit.

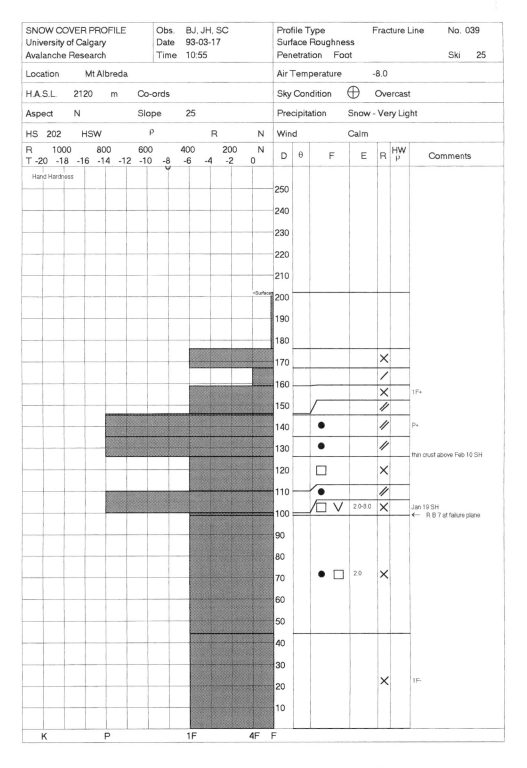

*Fig. 4.34  Fracture line profile observed one day after the incident on Mt. Albreda.*

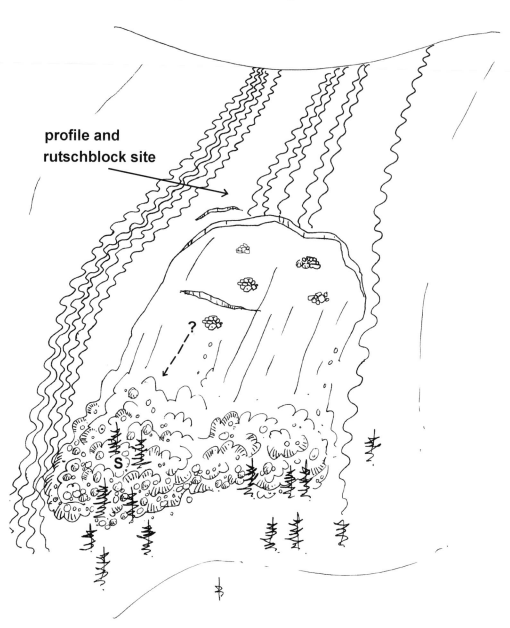

**profile and rutschblock site**

*Fig. 4.35 Mt. Albreda, 93-03-16. Given the stability of the weak layer at the profile and rutschblock site, it is likely that the slab was triggered from particularly weak snow near the rocks exposed by the avalanche. S - survivor.*

The 100 cm-thick slab released on the layer of surface hoar that had been buried on January 19th—two months earlier (Fig. 4.34). The next day, researchers working in the area travelled to the site to do stability tests. The most representative site available was about 2 m above the crown fracture where the incline was 25°. At this site, the rutschblock test resulted in a score of 7, suggesting stability. As well, a stability index calculated from a set of shear frame tests (Jamieson and Johnston, 1995a) also indicated stability.

The bed surface was unusual in that humps of the underlying moraine were exposed and a crack extended down from the bed surface. Depth hoar crystals surrounded the humps of rock.

**Comment:** The avalanche was likely triggered from the depth hoar surrounding one of the places where the moraine was exposed. Growth of depth hoar is generally associated with relatively strong temperature gradients within the snowpack. This avalanche inspired a group of researchers to study the effect of buried rocks on temperature within the surrounding snowpack (Gray and others, 1995). Other examples of triggering from depth hoar near rocks are described by Logan (1993).

Although the particular surface hoar layer was widespread throughout the Cariboos and Monashees, no avalanches were reported to have failed on this layer *for seven weeks*. The rutschblock and shear frame tests—which indicated stability—were probably within 20 m of the trigger point, illustrating that stability tests several metres away from a localised snowpack weakness can be misleading. Fractures that start at a localised weak spot can spread through weak layers which, in many places, cannot be triggered (Jamieson, 1995, pp. 185-194).

Stability and snow strength tests at well chosen sites generally yield useful information for assessing snowpack stability. Exceptions such as this case show that backcountry users should not base their decisions on snowpack tests alone. Even when tests and other field observations indicate stability, safety measures remain appropriate.

---

# Bruins Pass, Glacier National Park

17 March 1993

- **two backcountry skiers caught, one killed**
- **high avalanche danger**
- **weak faceted layer**

Two experienced ski-tourers were on a ski holiday to the Columbia Mountains in British Columbia. During the second week of March they had skied with a guide in the Esplanades just east of Glacier National Park. There they had witnesses avalanche activity and, even so, had tried to push the guide to ski more challenging runs. On March 15th they had skied up Glacier Crest and were again made aware of the high avalanche danger when they triggered a slide. On March 16th they had skied up Little Sifton and had found a sun crust on the south and west aspects that did not make for good skiing. Looking for better snow, they identified the east slope below Bruins Pass as a good place to ski the next day. A local skier advised them against the slope, pointing out its obvious dangers of steepness and lee orientation.

On the morning of the 17th they went to the warden station and read the weather and avalanche forecast. The stability was rated as *poor* —meaning that skiing in starting zones would likely produce avalanches. Nevertheless the two men proceeded up the Connaught drainage towards their objective of Bruins Pass. The weather was not very good with low cloud and snow obscuring some of the features around them. They made their way into the basin below Bruins Pass and then skied east and north across the bowl to the rock outcrops high on the east side. Staying close to the rock outcrops to minimise avalanche potential, they then traversed to the west and ascended the slope below the pass. Near the top the angle steepened and they progressed by making switch-backs.

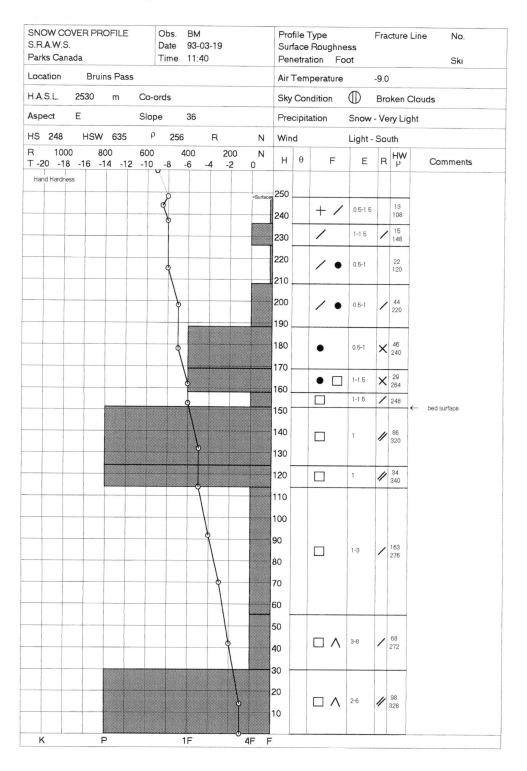

*Fig. 4.36 Fracture line profile at site of Bruins Pass avalanche observed two days after accident.*

They were not entirely comfortable on the slope; the history of the snowpack was making them nervous. The whole 1992-93 winter had been one of relatively little snow and cold temperatures. This had led to unusual amounts of faceting in the snowpack. In addition, ten days earlier, a warm storm with above zero temperatures had moved through the Columbia Mountains resulting in a major avalanche cycle. Following this, a colder air mass had invaded the region once again and had frozen the surface snow layer into a hard crust. This change in weather had also produced a little new snow which fell on top of the crust. The weather remained cool and dry during the next week, continuing the faceting process and then, on March 15th, over 25 cm of new snow fell in the park. Associated winds on that day and on the 16th were strong enough to transport some snow and load lee slopes in the alpine even more. By the morning of the 17th the conditions had deteriorated even further to produce the high avalanche danger.

One of the skiers wanted to turn back but the other one was determined to reach their objective and they kept going. They continued climbing up the east-facing slope to an elevation of about 2530 m. The wind-loaded lee slope was becoming even more serious, reaching an angle of 36°. They were only 15 m below the col, though, and they kept pushing onwards. The two skiers were at opposite ends of a switch-back when the lead skier went a little further to the left than before and started to do his last kick-turn needed to gain the ridge.

Unfortunately he had ventured out onto a pillow of snow on that side of the slope. His added weight caused a weak layer of facets down about 1 m to collapse and initiated an avalanche. Both men heard the whumpf and were immediately caught in the moving mass of snow. The avalanche, a size 2.5, fractured from the pass along the ridge to the south. It slid down about 1 m near the first skier and over into the shallower snow by the second skier, about 30 m away. The second skier released his bindings, threw off his pack and poles and made swimming motions to stay at the surface of the avalanche. He ended up about 300 m

downhill, but on the surface. Over where the first skier was, the deeper snow moved faster and carried him down about 800 m. He was able to discard his poles but his safety straps were attached to his boots and his bindings did not release. His pack also stayed on. He ended up buried face down, head downhill, under 0.5 to 1 m of snow.

The second skier started the search as soon as the avalanche came to a stop. His equipment had ended up on the surface, one pole above him but the rest below him in a straight line. He shouted out but received no reply. He took out his transceiver, switched to receive and then, as he had last seen his partner above and to his right, he started searching uphill. He did not get a signal, though, and turned around to zig-zag downhill. He picked up a signal in the lower third of the deposit and pinpointed his partner's location after searching for about 10 minutes. It took at least another 5 minutes to dig him out. When he uncovered him, his partner did not have any vital signs so he tried to resuscitate him for about 45 minutes but he did not respond. He skied back down to the pass and reported the accident to the park wardens.

The wardens went in by helicopter and spotted the body. With avalanche spotters watching for further activity, they moved the body another 800 m downhill by toboggan, but because the avalanche hazard was so high they decided to postpone the evacuation until the danger lessened. Two days later they were able to get to the site once more and evacuate the body. Afterwards a team flew up to the ridge near Bruins Pass to do a fracture line profile. As they were skiing towards the site they triggered a size 3.5 avalanche which ran on the same layer as the fatal accident two days prior. This avalanche was much larger than the first one and overran the evacuation site. None of the team was caught in the slide and they proceeded to do fracture line profiles near the crowns of both avalanches (Fig. 4.36).

Upon investigation it was found that the bed surface of the avalanches was a dense layer of faceted crystals that had initially been the hard crust mentioned earlier. Above this was a layer of loose unconsolidated facets which acted as

the weak layer that had collapsed. Above this were two layers of harder snow and then the decomposing and new snow from the past few days. The weak faceted layer that the snow slope had failed at was about 1 m below the surface.

**Source:** Eric Dafoe, Bruce McMahon, Glacier National Park

**Comment:** Although both skiers in this case had many years of backcountry skiing experience, the determination of the leading skier pushed the limits of safety too far. Under the current conditions—*high* avalanche danger—the steep wind-loaded slope should have been avoided.

The actions of the second skier were correct in that he discarded his gear when the avalanche started. Whether or not those same actions would have saved the first skier cannot be known. However, it is considered standard practice to not use safety straps when in avalanche terrain and likewise, to not have your pole straps around your wrists. Obviously, ski bindings should be releasable. Both skis and poles can act as anchors to pull you down into an avalanche or, at the very least, to increase the twisting forces on your arms and legs if you are caught in one. Heavy packs should be discarded since they hinder movement in an avalanche. However, a small light pack may actually give you more buoyancy as well as protect your back from injury.

---

# White Creek, Purcell Mountains

29 March 1993

- **one backcountry skier caught under apparently stable conditions**

In the southern Purcells, a group of three skiers was skiing a northeast facing slope above treeline on Mar 29th. Most of that particular slope had slid as size 1 and 2 slides on a layer of faceted grains that was buried in mid-February. On March 29th, the faceted layer could still be found in profiles of the snowpack but no avalanches had slid on this weak layer for two weeks. The skiers knew that the part of the slope they were considering had not slid on the faceted layer, but profiles and the lack of natural or human-triggered avalanche activity indicated stability.

Fortunately, the group decided to ski the slope one at a time. Skier 1 skied to a safe position at the bottom of an adjacent slope. Skier 2 began his run while Skier 3 waited at a safe place at the top of the slope. After skiing about 150 m, Skier 2 skied into an unsuspected pocket of moist faceted snow at the base of the steeper part of the slope and fell. There was a delay of 1-2 seconds before a 70 cm fracture

line propagated 110 m across a slight convexity near the top of the slope. Skier 2 was able to stand up and ride the avalanche for 30 m until it stopped. By the time the other skiers reached him, he had dug out the snow from around his legs. One ski had been lost but it was recovered by probing.

The size 2 slab avalanche extended 220 m from the fracture line to the toe of deposit. It had slid on the faceted layer (Fig. 4.37) that had been buried for six weeks and had not produced avalanches for two weeks. In rutschblock tests near the fracture line shortly after the avalanche, the faceted layer did not fail (score 7), also suggesting stability.

The fracture line profile shows a 5 cm-thick layer of faceted crystals 77 cm below the surface and depth hoar at the bottom of the pack. However, at the base of the slope where Skier 2 fell there was a 5 m-wide band across the slope where most of the snowpack was "rotten", consisting of facets and depth hoar. The skier caused a failure in this weak band which spread

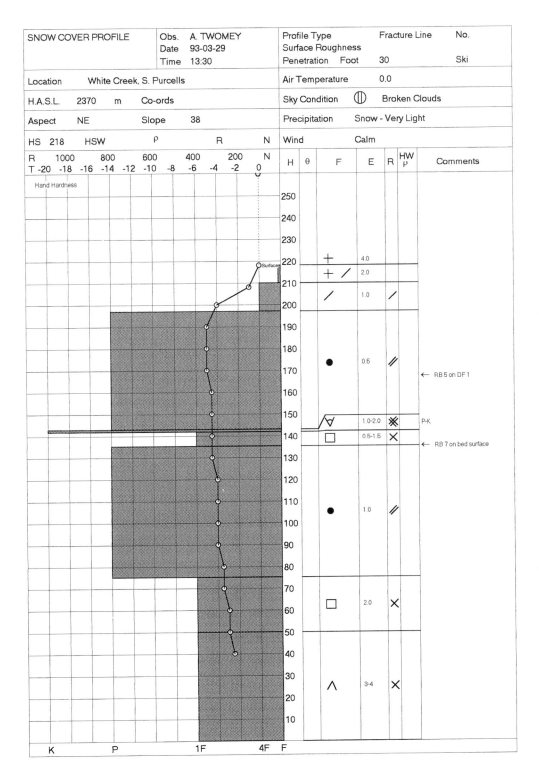

*Fig. 4.37 Fracture line profile at site of White Creek accident observed on the day of the incident.*

*Fig. 4.38 White Creek, 93-03-29. 1, 2, 3 - locations of skiers when avalanche started. Skier 2 triggered the avalanche in a pocket of weak snow and was caught but not injured. Art Twomey photo.*

up the slope along the six-week-old faceted layer (Fig. 4.38). There are no bushes or coarse talus under the rotten band that might explain the faceting band in the snowpack. However, in this valley there are geothermal warm spots that cause the snowpack to be locally thinner and more faceted. When air temperatures are particularly cold, steam drifts from the snowpack over these warm spots.

**Source:** Art Twomey

**Comment:** The rutschblock scores of 7 and the lack of avalanches indicate that the faceted weak layer was difficult to trigger in most places. However, once the fracture started where the snowpack was locally rotten, it spread along the seemingly stable faceted layer, releasing the slab avalanche. Such events are rare but support the use of safety measures even when snow conditions appear stable. The incident on 16 March 1993 at Mt. Albreda also illustrates a misleading snowpack test.

# Mt. Howard Douglas, Banff National Park

28 November 1993

- **one backcountry skier killed**
- **no transceivers and only one shovel**

Under cloudy skies with snow flurries, two skiers toured up from Bourgeau parking lot for a day of telemarking on the slopes near Sunshine Ski Village.

At about 13:30 in Howard Douglas Basin, they began ascending the north-facing slope to reach a well known slope to the south. Skier 1 was 30-35 m ahead of Skier 2, near the bottom of the slope when they triggered a size 2.5 slab avalanche on the slope above them. Skier 2 saw the snow surface crack open above him. He pointed his skis down to ski out of the avalanche but was quickly caught. When the ava-

lanche stopped he was only partly buried but it took 20 minutes to dig himself out, having lost his shovel in the slide.

Skier 2 called out but could not hear or see his partner. He began probing at the toe of the deposit and then saw his partner's boots and skis sticking out of the snow. Skier 2 dug out the victim's head which was 70 cm below the surface, facing down. Without a shovel, that took 20 minutes. He tried to clear the airway but it was solidly packed with snow. Using the victim's skis he skied to the mid station of the Sunshine Gondola to get help.

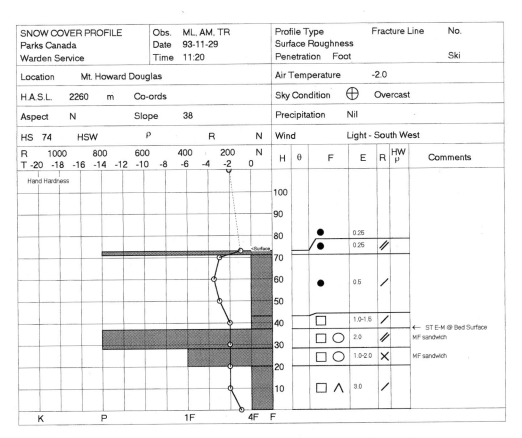

*Fig. 4.39 Fracture line profile observed the day after the accident on Mt. Howard Douglas.*

The Sunshine Ski Patrol and the Warden Service responded. A warden and paramedic were slung to the scene under a helicopter but the victim had asphyxiated.

The slab failed in a layer of faceted grains and slid on a melt-freeze crust (Fig. 4.39). The 75 m-long crown fracture averaged 60 cm in thickness and reached a maximum thickness of 150 cm. The north-facing start zone was at 2260 m and had an average incline of 38°.

**Source:** Banff Park Warden Service

**Comment:** The skiers chose to ascend an open slope adjacent to a treed slope.

The bulletin issued the day before noted that the avalanche hazard was *moderate* and that:

"There is a weak faceted base compounded by some early season crusts at elevations around treeline. The past storm has deposited enough snow to overload this base and a number of avalanches were observed on various aspects above treeline following the storm. Although little [avalanche] activity has been recorded in the past few days this instability is lingering and the weight of a skier may be enough to overload the slab above it."

Had the skiers done a snow profile or tested the snowpack near the slope, they might have found the instability noted in the bulletin and observed in the fracture line profile.

Unfortunately, Skier 2 lost his shovel. He could have dug out himself and his partner more quickly with a shovel.

---

# Greely Creek, Selkirk Mountains

22 February 1994

- **collisions with trees**

A group of heli-skiers was caught in a size 3 avalanche that came down on them from above. It was either triggered by a cornice fall or by the skiers themselves from below. Four people were partially buried and several others were carried along on the surface. The path of the avalanche, however, went through a forest and some of the people collided with trees and sustained injuries. The slab initially slid on 10 mm surface hoar but then stepped down into older snow. There were several unlinked crowns for a total width of about 500 m and depths ranging from 60 to 130 cm. One of those injured died in hospital a week later due to complications.

**Comment:** Obstacles such as trees in the avalanche path increase the risk of injury in an avalanche.

# Moat Lake, Strathcona Provincial Park

18 March 1994

- **small slide**
- **potentially deadly**

A group of skiers headed into Strathcona Provincial Park on Vancouver Island intending to ski the large slopes on the east side of Moat Lake. However, after testing some smaller slopes nearby they were scared off by the *easy* results they were getting. Still wanting to do some skiing, they made their way to a large bump near the outlet of the lake. Here they took turns jumping off a small cornice and getting in a few turns just above the lake.

It was still snowing lightly but it was clearing after the storm of the previous day. There was about 60 cm of fresh snow. The slope of the large bump was only about 25° and had a slightly concave shape to it.

When one of the skiers reached the cornice he stalled on the edge instead of jumping right off. His weight caused the cornice to break off and he fell forward, landing face first. A size 1.5 avalanche resulted and only carried him about 7.5 m down the slope, but it piled up debris to a depth of 160 cm. Both of his skis released but a wrist loop kept one pole attached to him. He ended up upside-down, twisted, with one hand over his mouth, one hand above his head and one foot sticking out of the snow. He was unable to move, everything was dark and he had trouble breathing in the dense snow.

His friends saw the whole event happen and although the snow had packed up, they were still able to quickly shovel him out. This only took one minute, but he was already blue and making sputtering and coughing noises. He quickly recovered, however.

**Source:** Niko Weis

**Comment:** Small slopes can slide just as easily as big ones and if enough snow moves, they can be just as deadly. The denser the snow the more dangerous it becomes as well. Less air gets through so asphyxiation can occur earlier. It also sets up more quickly, making movement impossible and digging more difficult. This shows why a shovel is such an important tool to carry. Digging with a shovel is many times more effective and can very well mean the difference between getting somebody out alive or dead.

# Europa Lake, Coast Mountains

21 May 1994

- **one ski-mountaineer killed**
- **small avalanche led to large consequence**
- **carried over cliff**

Five people were two weeks into a three week ski-mountaineering trip in the Coast Mountains south of Kitimat, British Columbia. Four of the group decided to ski up a 1850 m peak south of the east end of Europa Lake while one of them stayed with the packs. At one point while skiing up the mountain they needed to take off their skis to ascend a steep section about 15 m high. Above this the travel again became easier and they could ski the rest of the way to

*Fig. 4.40 Europa Lake, 94-05-21. Line of fall begins with small slide above cornice, then over the cornice triggering larger slide below which carried him over cliff. X - deceased landed on ledge part way down cliff face.*

the summit. On the descent, the first skier reached the steep section and decided to ski down instead of taking his skis off again.

It was cloudy. There was a wet mist in the air and the wind was light. The temperature was 0°C and, with it being late May, the snowpack had spring-like characteristics. The steep southeast-facing slope was convex and angled at 40°. The most significant factor, though, was that the slope ended in a cornice with another slope below that, ending in a 300 m cliff.

When the skier made a turn on the steep section he released a small, wet, loose slide. It was only about 10 cm thick and 8 m wide, but it was enough to make him lose his edge control and it knocked him into a sitting position. Unable to control his descent, he was carried down over the cornice and landed hard on the slope below. This impact released another avalanche, some 35 cm deep by 15 m wide, that carried him over the edge of the 300 m cliff.

"We raced back to [the fifth member] at the packs, set off our PLT and skied around to the next valley which put us at the base of the rock face where we found his smashed pieps and camera." A rescue helicopter arrived the next morning to evacuate the survivors and saw the victim's body two-thirds of the way down the rock face on a ledge. It was another four days until a Parks Canada rescue team, in difficult weather conditions, was able to pluck him off the cliff using a helicopter and 15 m long-line. The skier had died from trauma as a result of his fall down the cliff.

**Source:** John Clarke

**Comment:** Slopes need to be assessed not only for their potential to avalanche, but also for the consequences of an avalanche, even a small one. Whether a slope ends in low angled terrain, a gully, or a cliff, must factor into decision making. A slight loss of control in an unforgiving location can spell disaster.

# Hemlock Valley Ski Area, BC

19 November 1994

- **one ski patroller killed**
- **no transceiver**

| Date | Max. | Min. | Snowfall | Rain |
|------|------|------|----------|------|
| Weather Conditions at Agassiz Research Station Elevation 25 m, 19 km southeast of accident site | | | | |
| 1994 | Temp. | Temp. | | |
| | (°C) | (°C) | (cm) | (mm) |
| 11-15 | 7.0 | 4.5 | 0 | 16.2 |
| 11-16 | 4.0 | 1.5 | 1.0 | 14.8 |
| 11-17 | 6.0 | 0.0 | - | freezing rain |
| 11-18 | 2.0 | -1.5 | 1.0 | 4.8 |
| 11-19 | 6.5 | -1.5 | 0.1 | 18.5 |

On November 19th, before the Hemlock Valley Ski Area opened for the winter of 1994-95, ski patrollers were assessing the snow stability, using explosives to release unstable snow on some slopes.

Hemlock Valley Ski Area is 70 km east of North Vancouver and 22 km north of Chilliwack. Heavy snow fall in mid-November 1994 resulted in a deeper-than-average snowpack consisting of 210 cm of relatively unconsolidated snow. Approximately 20 cm of snow fell during the 18th and morning of the 19th. Also, the air temperature in the ski area was about 4 degrees warmer than the day before, and approached 0°C. Conditions were ripe for avalanches.

At about 14:30, two patrollers on skis accessed the top of Crans Bowl. One patroller stayed near the top of the bowl while the other skied down a slight ridge. After observing an avalanche in the bowl, the patroller at the top could no longer see her partner. She skied down to the deposit, realised he was buried and called for help.

Ski area staff responded in snow cats. Since the victim was not wearing a transceiver, they began probing. The storm continued with mixed rain and snow blown by moderate to strong winds. Over the next 2.5 hours, the search team grew to 40 people and two police dogs. Finally, the victim's body was located by probing near where a search dog had indicated. The victim was in a vertical position, under 1.5 m of snow at a transition in the slope above a cat road (Fig. 4.41). At this site, the deposit was deeper than average .

The 45 m-wide slab avalanche started in a 40° section of a shallow southeast-facing bowl. It ran down a 34° slope in the bowl and reached size 2 . The slab failed on a weak layer of storm snow consisting of decomposing and fragmented particles. The thickness of the slab averaged 30 cm and reached a maximum of 70 cm.

**Source:** Chris Stethem, Anton Horvath, Hemlock Valley Ski Area, Chilliwack RCMP and *The Vancouver Sun*, 12 November 1994

**Comment:** Although many pronounced ridges are preferred routes during unstable conditions, slight ridges such as in this accident offer little protection from avalanches. This case illustrates the importance of route selection.

The victim was not wearing a transceiver, which is basic equipment for avalanche control on skis. Also, the victim was buried in a vertical position, reducing the odds of successful probing.

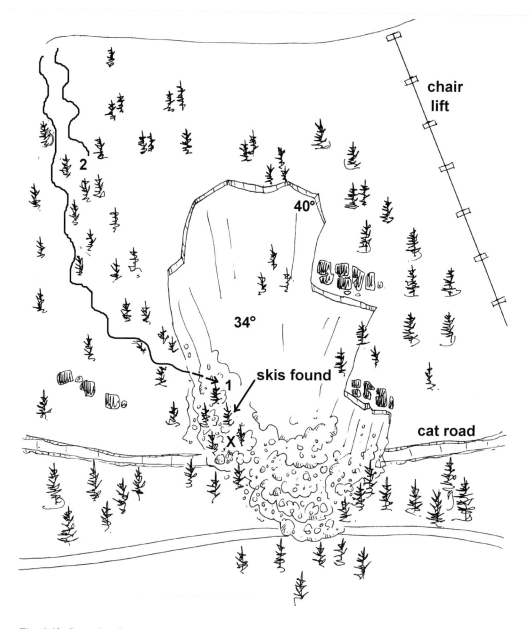

*Fig. 4.41 Crans Bowl at Hemlock Valley Ski Area, 94-11-19. 1, 2 - approximate locations of skiers when avalanche started. The body of the first skier was found at X where the deposit piled up deeply at a transition just above a cat road.*

# Mount Ryder, near McBride, BC

4 February 1995

- **one helicopter skier killed**
- **isolated weakness**
- **deep burial**

Three heli-skiers and their guide were on the eastern slopes of Mount Ryder, northwest of McBride, British Columbia. At 13:15 they were skiing at an elevation of 2130 m and reached a point where the group needed to cross a gully. The guide instructed the skiers to cross spaced well apart and then skied across the slope. The second skier crossed safely.

In the previous few days a small storm had deposited about 15 cm of new snow in the area. This storm snow had settled rapidly due to moderate temperatures and in most places seemed to be bonding well to the old snow underneath. The snow stability did not raise undue concern and subsequent stability tests on the slope also gave no indication of unstable layers.

As the last two skiers were crossing the slope, the fourth skier came fairly close to the skier in front of him. At this point the top 15 cm of the snowpack released. The avalanche then stepped down further into the snowpack to release down to a depth of 75 cm. The result was a size 2.5 avalanche. Both skiers were caught. However, the third skier was just at the edge of the slide and managed to stay on the surface.

The fourth skier was not as lucky and was swept down for about 360 m and ended up buried under 4 m of snow.

The guide immediately started rescue procedures and requested help by radio from a second guide also on the mountain, as well as calling in the helicopter. They skied down to the deposit and quickly located the victim by avalanche transceiver and probe. Once his exact location was known he was dug out as quickly as possible, but due to the great depth of burial it took 25 minutes to uncover him. The victim was unresponsive so CPR was initiated and he was flown by helicopter to McBride Hospital. He was pronounced dead by asphyxiation.

**Comment:** Isolated weaknesses in the snowpack continue to be one of the most difficult things to identify and assess. Snow profiles and tests can only give results for the immediate area where they are being done and therefore are not positive indicators for the entire slope. The risks associated with encountering one of these isolated weaknesses are part of the infinite variability of nature and must be accepted as such.

# Burstall Pass, Kananaskis Country

19 February 1995

- **five backcountry skiers caught, two completely buried and one killed**
- **recent snowfall and wind loading**
- **extreme avalanche danger**
- **party not adequately equipped for self-rescue**

| Date 1995 | Max. Temp. (°C) | Min. Temp. (°C) | Snowfall (cm) | Storm Snow (cm) | Snowpack Height (cm) | Wind |
|---|---|---|---|---|---|---|
| 02-14 | -13.0 | -33.0 | 0 | 0 | 98 | L - S |
| 02-15 | -20.0 | -20.0 | 0 | 0 | 98 | L - S |
| 02-16 | -10.0 | -20.0 | 2 | 2 | 98 | L - NW |
| 02-17 | -6.0 | -10.0 | 19 | 20 | 117 | Calm |
| 02-19 | 0.5 | -6.5 | 24 | 32 | 129 | L - NE |

Weather Conditions at Chester Lake Trail Head at 08:00
Elevation 1905 m, 7 km NE of accident site

Burstall Pass is a popular one-day ski tour in Kananaskis Country. Within a couple of hours from the trailhead, skiers can enjoy the view from the pass and ski the nearby slopes.

On February 19th, a group of 12 skiers left the Spray Lakes Road in Kananaskis Country and toured up the trail towards Burstall Pass. After four turned around, the remaining eight continued toward the often windy pass.

The previous week had been generally clear and cold with overnight lows down to -33°C. The surface hoar that formed in sheltered areas during the week was buried by heavy snowfall that started on Thursday the 16th and continued through the weekend. On the morning of Sunday the 19th, the posted avalanche danger near and above treeline in Kananaskis Country was increased from *high* to *extreme* due to heavy snowfall and extensive wind loading of lee slopes. Although snowfall was light, strong west winds loaded the east-facing slopes just below Burstall Pass.

After having lunch below the pass, the group of eight skiers started to ascend the final slope. Concerned about the cornice at the top of the slope they decided to drop part way down the slope to some trees. As they started to descend, a hard slab avalanche released just be-

low the cornice, catching the first five of the eight skiers. "When it started, it looked so harmless. I thought nothing of it." Skier 3 was able to "swim" since she had just put on mitts too bulky for her pole straps. Also, one of her bindings tore out of the ski, freeing one leg. When the avalanche stopped, Skier 1 was on the edge of the deposit and only buried to his knees. Skiers 2 and 3 could not be seen. Skier 4 was buried to her waist. The fifth skier only had an arm sticking out of the snow but was able to clear the snow from around her face. (Fig. 4.42).

A party of three and a party of two other skiers observed the avalanche and came to assist with probes and shovels. Within 3 minutes they dug out Skiers 4 and 5. Since the two remaining victims were not wearing transceivers, the searchers began to probe the deposit. Skier 3 was found and freed from under 1 m of deposited snow, 20 minutes after the avalanche. She regained consciousness, was treated for hypothermia and later recovered. Skier 2 was found under 2 m of snow 40 minutes after the avalanche. CPR was done for 30 minutes but he did not recover. Kananaskis Country Rangers, who had been notified by a third group

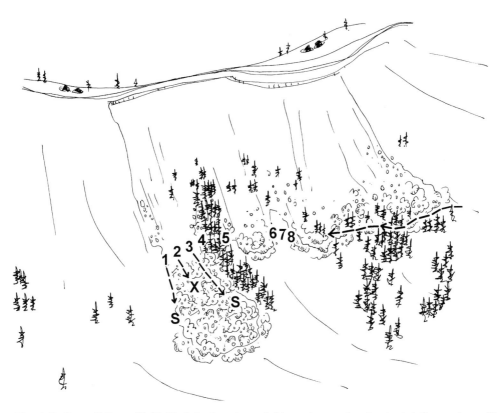

*Fig. 4.42  Burstall Pass, 95-02-19. 1-8 - locations of skiers when avalanche started. S - survivors. X - deceased.*

that saw the avalanche, evacuated most members of the accident party by helicopter.

The size 2 dry slab avalanche started on a 41° east-facing slope just under the cornice at 2380 m. The crown averaged 50 cm in thickness and was 175 m wide. The air temperature had warmed to -1°C at 13:30 when the avalanche occurred.

**Source:** Burke Duncan and Larry Stanier, Kananaskis Country; Andy Vollmerhaus, Calgary.

**Comment:** The party was not adequately equipped for avalanche rescue. The prompt response by the nearby group with rescue equipment probably saved the third skier's life.

The avalanche danger was rated as *extreme* on the day of the accident and *high* the day before. Wind-loading of the slope above the skiers was evident. The group recognised the hazard but did not descend soon enough to avoid the avalanche hazard.

Many people who are attracted to the mountains seek destinations such as peaks or passes. This goal-seeking may cause the option of turning around to be overlooked.

# Marmot Peak, Jasper National Park

15 March 1995

- **one out-of-bounds skier killed**
- **no transceivers, only one shovel**
- **persistent weak layer in old snow**
- *considerable* **avalanche danger**

| Date 1995 | Time | Max. Temp. (°C) | Min. Temp. (°C) | Sky Condition | Snowfall (cm) | Total Snowpack (cm) | Wind (km/h) |
|---|---|---|---|---|---|---|---|
| | | | | Weather Conditions at Marmot Basin Ski Area | | | |
| | | | | Elevation 1980 m, 2 km from accident site | | | |
| 03-12 | 0755 | 2.5 | -6.5 | Broken | 1 | 119 | 20 - SW |
| 03-13 | 0745 | 3.0 | -10.0 | Clear | 0.1 | 118 | 9 - SW |
| 03-14 | 0745 | 1.0 | -10.0 | Broken | 0.1 | 116 | 22 - SW |
| 03-15 | 0745 | 3.0 | -7.5 | Scattered | 4 | 118 | 25 - SW |

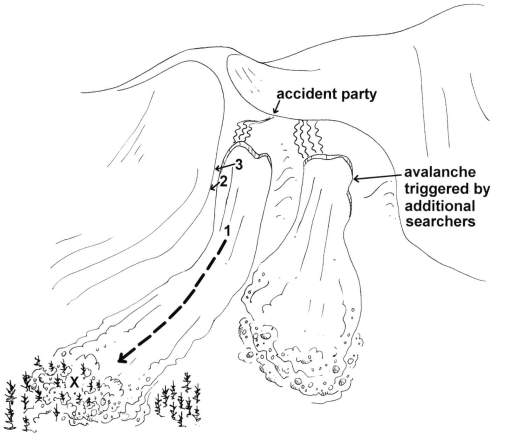

*Fig. 4.43 Marmot Peak, 95-03-15. Skier 1 was found at X. Skiers 2 and 3 escaped to the side. Additional searchers coming to assist the rescue triggered the slide to the right of the first avalanche.*

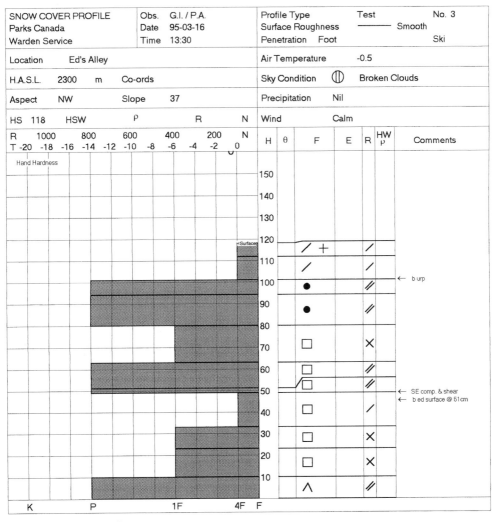

Stability Assessment: Poor
Test confirms layers found on shallow borders of the slide path. Almost as if the new storm snow that formed the slab is so well bonded to layers below that it ripped everything out to the faceted layers below (first significant weakness).

*Fig. 4.44 Profile observed on the day after the accident. Shovel and compression tests resulted in easy shear.*

On the afternoon of March 15th, three skiers left the Marmot Basin Ski Area to ski Ed's Alley on the northwest side of Marmot Peak. The upper half of Ed's Alley is a 37-40° wind-loaded basin. Below a bench, the lower half is a 35-37° cross-loaded gully.

In the previous 24 hours, 4 cm of snow had fallen during light to moderate southwest winds.

At about 14:00, when all three skiers were about one quarter of the way down the gully below the bench, a slab avalanche released. The middle skier had stopped off to the side of the gully, while the other two were skiing, one 20 m above and the other below the stationary skier. The top and middle skier escaped to the side. The avalanche carried the lower skier down 300 m and buried him under 30 cm of snow.

The two survivors skied down and searched the deposit visually. Not seeing any sign of their partner, one stayed to probe the deposit with a ski pole while the other returned to the ski area to get help.

Marmot Basin staff were notified at 15:30, went to the scene and began probing the deposit. A search dog and master from the ski area arrived at 16:28 and found the victim in 15 minutes, just as Jasper Park Wardens arrived in a helicopter with a second dog team. Rescuers started advanced resuscitation efforts and flew the victim to Jasper where he was pronounced dead.

Shortly after the victim was found, seven additional searchers from the ski area were approaching the accident site from above when they triggered a second slab avalanche beside the first one. They moved out of its way and were not injured.

The 60 cm-thick slab from the first avalanche failed on a layer of faceted crystals, leaving a 75 m-wide crown fracture on a 34-37° start zone (Fig. 4.44). The deposit from the size 2 avalanche had an average depth of 2 m and a maximum depth of 3.4 m.

**Source:** Jasper Park Warden Service, Marmot Basin Ski Area and *The Edmonton Journal*, 17 March 1995.

**Comment:** All three skiers could have been buried since they were in the gully at the same time.

The ski area rated the avalanche danger as *considerable*. This information was posted at the ski area. Jasper National Park rated the backcountry avalanche danger as *high* and explicitly warned of wind-loaded areas. The second avalanche provided further indication of the unstable conditions.

The victim was only buried under about 30 cm of snow; transceivers and shovels would have allowed the survivors to find the buried victim quickly. No one in the party had transceivers and only the buried victim had a shovel.

The first dogmaster to arrive was a member of the Canadian Avalanche Rescue Dog Association. The volunteer members of CARDA respond to many accidents every year.

# Robertson, Quebec

22 December 1995

- **two backcountry skiers killed**
- **open pit mine**

Late on the 22nd two young men made their way towards a tailings pile at an open pit mine with intentions to ski a slope approximately 135 m high. The abandoned asbestos mine lies some 150 km northwest of Montreal.

The accident was unwitnessed but the evidence suggests the following scenario. The men had their skis strapped to their backs and were making their way up the 35° slag heap when they triggered a moist slide that slid on the ground. They were both caught by the avalanche and completely buried, ending up face down with their skis still on their backs.

When they had not returned by nightfall, a friend went to look for them. When he saw that an avalanche had occurred at the site where the

two had intended to ski, he went back for help. A search party of 30 people made up of police, fire-fighters and volunteers travelled to the site. Using shovels and long poles as probes they finally found the two men at about 23:00. They were found buried under 1 m of snow and, although they had been buried for an estimated 6 hours, they were resuscitated, although they remained unconscious. Unfortunately, both died in hospital later that night.

**Comment:** Usually considered a mountain phenomena, avalanches can and do occur in less obvious places. Any slope that is steep enough, is large enough, and has enough snow on it to slide, can create an avalanche big enough to kill.

# No Name Ridge, Stagleap Provincial Park

4 January 1996

- **one fatality**
- **alone when buried**

Four skiers and snowboarders started their day at Summit Lake on the Salmo-Creston Highway in southeastern British Columbia. The area is popular with backcountry skiers because of good skiing quite close to the road. They skied and snowshoed in for about 2 km to No Name Ridge and did a couple of runs on it. One of the snowboarders was not feeling very well and decided to return to the lake by himself. He started hiking back on his snowshoes and came across a steep slope that he could not cross at his present elevation. He made a down-hill switchback and entered the slope lower down, where it was not quite as steep. The steep section of the slope he avoided was 37° and where he was crossing was 34°.

Back in late December a clear spell in the weather had formed a surface hoar layer. This was following by a series of storms from December 29th to January 3rd which had buried the weak layer. Cold temperatures had also faceted the upper layers of the snowpack. It was just waiting for a trigger.

*Fig. 4.45 No Name Ridge, 96-01-04. X - deceased.*

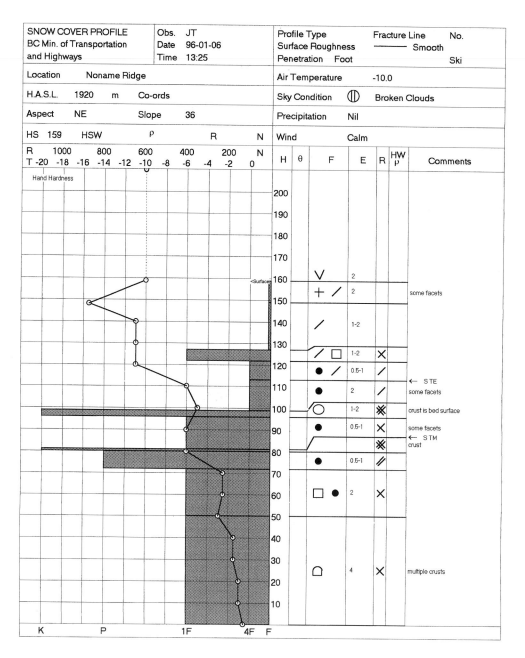

*Fig. 4.46 Fracture line profile on No Name Ridge observed two days after the accident.*

As the snowboarder stepped into the concave zone of the slope, an avalanche released a few metres above him. The size 2 avalanche released from one rock outcrop to the other, over a width of 25 m and down to the surface hoar layer, 35 to 60 cm below the surface. He was knocked over and carried down the slope, coming to a stop above a large rock outcrop where the snow was piling up (Fig. 4.45). His head was buried under 1 m of snow but his arm was still sticking out above the surface. He was wearing an avalanche transceiver. He could not move.

When his friends came by the avalanche site some 45 minutes later they saw his arm sticking out and quickly dug him out. They started CPR, but after 20 minutes without results, they stopped.

Avalanche technicians for the BC Ministry of Transportation and Highways responded to the accident. They flew in by helicopter and side-slipped down the avalanche bed surface to where the body lay. They rigged an 18 m long-line and the helicopter slung the body back to the trailhead.

**Source:** John Tweedy, BC Ministry of Transportation and Highways

**Comment:** Under certain conditions a concave zone on a slope can be very sensitive. Safer travel past such a feature would involve a route further down from the change in slope angle. Travelling alone, no matter how briefly, is obviously much riskier than in a group.

# Smugglers Ridge, Kokanee Glacier Park

26 February 1996

- **solo backcountry skier killed**
- **convex roll**

At 07:00 on the morning of the 26th, the hut-keeper for the Slocan Chief Cabin in Kokanee Glacier Park, British Columbia went out to take the daily weather readings. He then called the Canadian Avalanche Centre to pass on these readings as well as observations about snow conditions. A little later that morning he accompanied a new group to show them the way up Smugglers Ridge. When they reached about 2300 m he left the group and skied alone down the west side of the ridge towards Kokanee Pass to meet up with two friends that were skiing up to visit him.

The weather that day was clear, cold and calm as the region was under the influence of an arctic air-mass. In the past week it had snowed almost every day, accumulating 64 cm on top of a melt-freeze crust that had formed the previous week. Temperatures for the first three days of the storm had been just below zero and had caused the storm snow to quickly settle into a dense slab. Near the end of the storm, temperatures had dropped as the arctic front approached and the wind had shifted from the southwest to the north, causing reverse loading of slopes in the area.

He started skiing down Smugglers Ridge shortly after 10:00 and was out of sight of the group he had just left. Skiing through open trees, his route took him over a steep 42° convex roll at which point he started a size 2 slab avalanche. It fractured 45 m wide and about 50 cm deep, sliding on the melt-freeze crust and possibly on some small surface hoar sitting on the crust. He was carried through a small stand of mature timber and then on down the slope for about 200 m (Fig. 4.47). He came to a stop near the bottom of the avalanche, buried except for one bare hand sticking out above the snow.

At about 15:00 the hut-keeper's two friends passed by the slope and noticed the avalanche deposit but, due to the flat light, did not see his tracks leading into it, or anything else out of the ordinary. They continued on to the hut, reaching it by about 16:00. At 19:00 the group the hut-keeper had skied with that morning arrived back at the hut, at which time it became apparent that he was missing. They radioed the hut contractor in Nelson for assistance and then formed a rescue party equipped with headlamps. At 21:00 seven searchers set out from the hut and more help was on its way up from

ski tracks enter here

X

*Fig. 4.47 Smugglers Ridge, 96-02-26. X - deceased.*

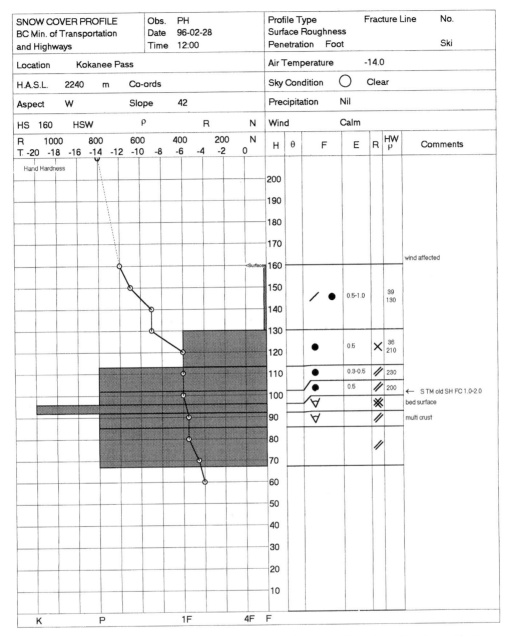

*Fig. 4.48  Fracture line profile at Smuggler's Ridge avalanche observed two days after the accident.*

Nelson by snowmobile. Ski tracks believed to be the hut-keeper's were found leading into the avalanche and using transceivers the rescuers were able to get close enough to see his hand sticking out. At 23:15 his body was dug out from under 60 cm of snow.

**Source:** Paul Heikkila, BC Ministry of Transportation and Highways and Kevin Giles, Kokanee Glacier Mountaineering

**Comment:** When skiing alone you are often accepting a much higher risk than if skiing with others. If something goes wrong there is no one there to help you so it becomes imperative that you choose terrain that is more forgiving.

# Bearpaw Ridge, near Longworth, BC

28 February 1996

- **one burial**
- **found by transceiver**
- **subsequent avalanche**

A man and his 23-year-old son climbed up to a ridge to ski the north-facing slope on the other side. They started up the south-facing slope from a logging operation some 10 km from Longworth, British Columbia. When they reached the top of the ridge they dug a snow pit to appraise the snow stability. They found 15 cm of soft snow on top of 55 cm of harder snow with a crust at the base of the hard snow layer. They did shovel shear tests and had *moderate* results at both the interface at 15 cm down and at the crust, 70 cm below the surface. Although this caused them some concern, the son was still eager to ski the slope. The father did not feel he could handle the steepness of the slope and decided, instead, to watch from the top. As his son approached the edge of the ridge he had a strong feeling that something was wrong. He thought about suggesting that his son not ski the slope, but then decided against it.

The sky was partly cloudy and a strong southerly wind was blowing over the ridge. The temperature was about -8°C. The slope was 500 m long, had an angle of 40° and a 1.5 m cornice at the top.

The son jumped off the cornice, landed on the slope and continued to ski down. When he was about two-thirds of the way down he triggered a small avalanche comprising the top 15 cm of snow. It started carrying him downhill but he was still able to move to the side. A couple of seconds later a larger avalanche started from just below the cornice. It fractured over a width of about 450 m and down to the crust they had found at 70 cm. This larger avalanche rapidly engulfed him and carried him to the bottom of the slope. When the snow stopped moving he found himself completely buried lying face down. He was able to make a small air space in front of his face but the weight of the 1.5 m of snow above him made it very hard to breathe and he passed out.

The father, meanwhile, had seen the whole scene unfold and he hastily made his way down to the deposit to where he had last seen his son. They were wearing avalanche transceivers and he was thus able to locate the burial spot. Fortunately he was also the one carrying their only shovel and he quickly dug down through the 1.5 m of snow to where he could uncover his son's head. At this point his son regained consciousness. About 30 minutes had passed since the avalanche had started.

One of the son's skis had ripped off with the binding still attached to his boot. The other ski had stayed on. This had caused his legs to be severely twisted during the avalanche but he did not suffer any serious injuries. They could not, however, find the lost ski.

They started to climb back up the slope in the avalanche track but found the hard bed surface difficult to climb on. They traversed over to the side of the slide and climbed up the undisturbed snow on the flanks. When they had nearly reached the top of the ridge, the snow around them released as well and carried them 100 m back down the slope. This avalanche only buried them up to the waist and they were able to extricate themselves and continue up to the ridge and back down the other side to the logging operation.

**Source:** George Evanoff

**Comment:** The snow at the sides of an avalanche can be as ready to slide as the snow that has just slid. In this case it would probably have been better if they had stayed on the bed surface instead of moving into the undisturbed snow on their climb back up.

The desire to ski a slope can, at times, overshadow better judgement. In this case the slope that avalanched had definite signs of instability. The cornice clearly indicated that the north side was a lee slope and that considerable loading had occurred. This was further implied by the strong south wind. The steepness of the slope made this all the more relevant.

In this case, the shovel test result and the father's intuition both questioned the stability of the slope and should not have been discounted. Without the effective transceiver search, the son's eagerness could have been fatal.

# Chapter 5

# Snowmobiling Accidents

## Onion Mountain, near Smithers, BC

23 February 1985

- **one fatality**
- **high pointing at night**

It was snowing heavily at just after midnight on Onion Mountain near Smithers, British Columbia. A number of snowmobilers were taking turns running up one of its slopes. When it was his turn, the victim started up the slope and was travelling at a high speed when he was hit by an avalanche. The avalanche was about 350 m wide and ran about 400 m. Neither the victim nor his snowmobile were buried in the slide, but when the other members of the group found him he had died of massive trauma.

**Comment:** When travelling in avalanche terrain it is important to hear and see what is happening around you.

## Mt. Erris, near Elkford, BC

2 March 1985

- **one snowmobiler killed**
- **group poorly equipped for self rescue**

Along the divide of the Rocky Mountains south of Banff National Park, a surface hoar layer had been buried by light snowfalls in late January or early February 1985. Strong north and northwest winds had added considerable load to lee slopes. On March 2nd, at Line Creek Mine 1550 m above sea level and 8 km north

of Mt. Erris, the temperature warmed from -15°C to -3°C. Winds were calm and no snow was falling.

At 11:15, five snowmobilers on four snowmobiles were traversing the southwest slopes of Mt. Erris, 22 km southeast of Elkford, BC. While crossing a slight gully at 2300 m,

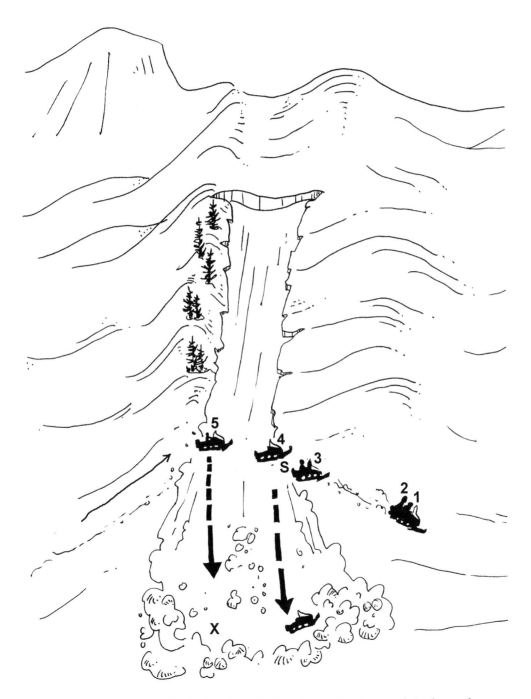

*Fig. 5.1 Mt. Erris, 85-03-02. 1 to 5 - locations of riders when avalanche started. X - deceased.*

the second snowmobile got stuck. An avalanche hit the fourth and fifth snowmobilers while they were stopped behind the second. The fourth rider escaped to the side but his snowmobile was carried down-slope. The fifth rider and his snowmobile were carried down to the deposit and buried (Fig. 5.1).

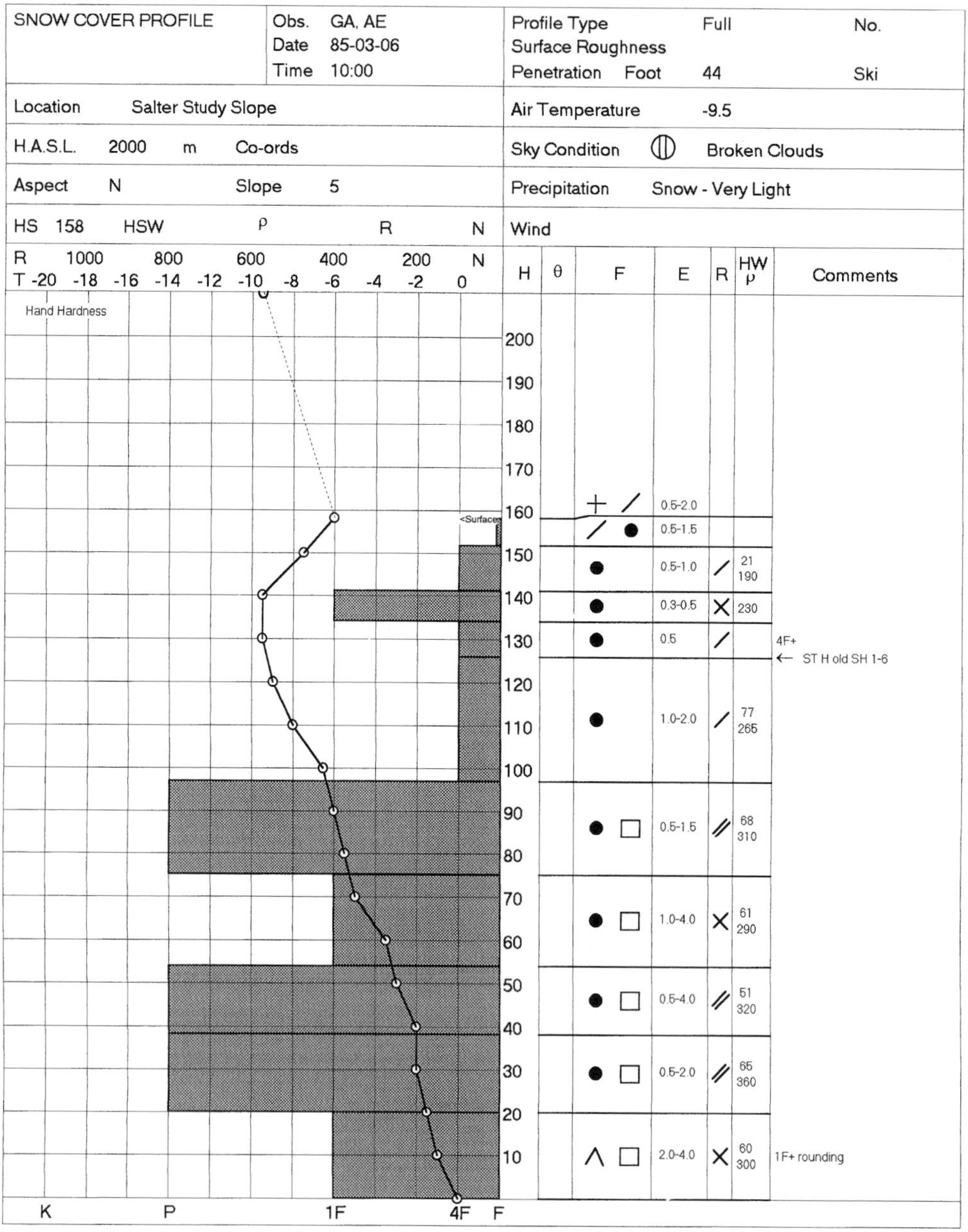

| SNOW COVER PROFILE | Obs. GA, AE | Profile Type | Full | No. |
| | Date 85-03-06 | Surface Roughness | | |
| | Time 10:00 | Penetration Foot 44 | | Ski |
| Location Salter Study Slope | | Air Temperature | -9.5 | |
| H.A.S.L. 2000 m Co-ords | | Sky Condition ⌽ Broken Clouds | | |
| Aspect N Slope 5 | | Precipitation Snow - Very Light | | |
| HS 158 HSW ρ R N | | Wind | | |

Profile data:

| R 1000 800 600 400 200 N | | | | | |
| T -20 -18 -16 -14 -12 -10 -8 -6 -4 -2 0 | | | | | |
| Hand Hardness | H | θ | F | E | R | HW ρ | Comments |
|---|---|---|---|---|---|---|---|
| | 160 <Surface> | + / | / | 0.5-2.0 | | | |
| | | / ● | | 0.5-1.5 | | | |
| | 150 | ● | | 0.5-1.0 | / | 21 190 | |
| | 140 | ● | | 0.3-0.5 | X | 230 | |
| | 130 | ● | | 0.5 | / | | 4F+ ← ST H old SH 1-6 |
| | 110 | ● | | 1.0-2.0 | / | 77 265 | |
| | 90 | ● □ | | 0.5-1.5 | // | 68 310 | |
| | 70/60 | ● □ | | 1.0-4.0 | X | 61 290 | |
| | 50 | ● □ | | 0.5-4.0 | // | 51 320 | |
| | 30 | ● □ | | 0.5-2.0 | // | 65 360 | |
| | 10 | ∧ □ | | 2.0-4.0 | X | 60 300 | 1F+ rounding |

K    P    1F    4F    F

*Fig. 5.2 Mt. Erris. Profile at Salter Study Plot, 4 km north of accident site and 4 days after accident, showing the shear on the surface hoar layer.*

Since the buried snowmobiler did not have a transceiver, the others used small trees to probe for him. After 40 minutes, they found the victim's body under 70 cm of snow near the toe of the deposit. He had suffocated.

The 20 m-wide slab averaged 30 cm in thickness and reached a maximum of 40 cm. It failed on the surface hoar layer that had been buried about a month earlier. The size 2.5 avalanche resulted in a deposit 75 m long and 35 m wide.

**Source:** Greg Allen

**Comment:** Three snowmobilers were stopped in a lee pocket at the same time. Had they been further apart, at most one would have been caught.

Although some of the riders had transceivers, others did not. Also, the group had no probes. Proper rescue equipment would have sped the search and increased the odds of recovering the victim alive.

At the Salter Study Plot, 4 km to the north of the accident site, the surface hoar was observed to shear in profiles observed twice a month. The shear was *easy* on February 13th, *hard* on March 6th and *easy* on April 2nd.

# Clemina Creek, Monashee Mountains

29 March 1986

- **four snowmobilers killed**
- **high hazard**
- **heavy snowfall and warm temperatures**
- **persistent weak layer in old snow**
- **no transceivers**

Clemina Creek is a popular snowmobiling area in the Monashee Mountains about 50 km south of Valemount, BC. On March 29th, a party of 11 people were snowmobiling up the Clemina Valley.

Strong winds, warm temperatures and 45 cm of snowfall at higher elevations had created an unstable snowpack. "Conditions were just right for avalanches."

The eleven riders were spread out along the trail when a kilometre-wide avalanche released 500 m above them. The avalanche hit the first six snowmobilers, completely burying five of them and partly burying one (Fig. 5.3).

Within about five minutes, the riders from the back of the group dug out the partly buried person, who was unharmed. They also quickly located a completely buried woman from articles on the surface of the deposit. A messenger

went out to the highway and notified the RCMP who contacted two nearby helicopter skiing operations and Jasper Park Wardens. When the first helicopter arrived, the buried woman was flown to hospital in McBride where she later recovered. During the afternoon, a total of 25 rescuers from the RCMP, helicopter skiing companies and national parks arrived on the scene to search for the remaining people. Two dogs also arrived but were not effective, perhaps because of the scent of fuel from the numerous sleds on the deposit. Two more victims were found that afternoon by probing. They had suffocated. The search was called off half an hour after dark.

At 06:30 the next morning, searchers returned with three search dogs and metal detectors. By probing, they located the bodies of the two remaining victims at 09:00 and 10:15. They had suffocated under 4 m of snow.

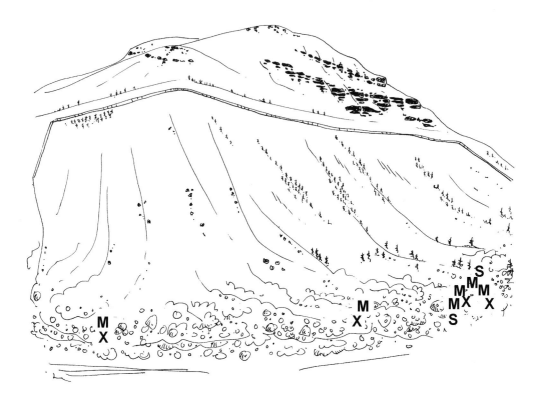

*Fig. 5.3 Clemina Creek, 86-03-29. The avalanche was approximately 1 km wide. M - snowmobile. X - deceased. S - survivor.*

The 1 m-thick slab failed on a layer of faceted crystals (Fig. 5.4). The bed surface of the size 3.5 avalanche stepped down, picking up additional snow and depositing up to 10 m of snow in the valley.

**Source:** Jasper Park Warden Service and *The Vancouver Sun*, 31 March 1986

**Comment:** In spite of the danger created by the combination of precipitation, wind and warming, the group rode their machines through the runout zones of large avalanche paths. Other groups cancelled their trips into the mountains that weekend because of the danger. At the time, no public avalanche bulletin was available for the Monashees. However, the avalanche hazard in nearby Jasper National Park was rated *high*.

The group had no transceivers that would have enabled the survivors to quickly search for the buried victims, increasing the odds of finding them alive.

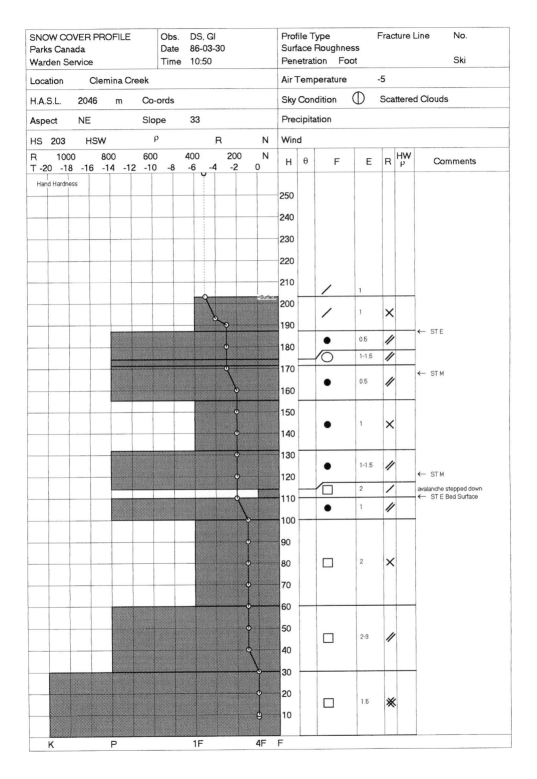

*Fig. 5.4 Clemina Creek fracture line profile observed one day after accident.*

# Middle Kootenay Pass, near Pincher Creek, Alberta

4 January 1989

- **one snowmobiler killed**
- **high-marking**
- **weak depth hoar layer**

A group of 14 snowmobilers were high-marking on a slope in the Middle Kootenay Pass area near Pincher Creek, Alberta. This is a popular snowmobiling area and lies just a few kilometres south of the Westcastle Ski Area. They were taking turns accelerating over a cleared well site and then riding up a steep slope.

The avalanche danger that day was extreme with a 40 cm-thick layer of very weak depth hoar at the base of the snowpack.

After taking repeated runs at the slope, one of the riders triggered a large avalanche which swept down the slope and caught three of the snowmobilers. The avalanche appeared to release at the base of the 150 cm-deep snowpack, in the depth hoar layer. Two riders were only partially buried but one snowmobiler and his snowmobile were completely buried.

Some of the group went to help the partially buried members, while the others cut branches from nearby trees to use as probes. One witness was sent to the ski hill for help. Ski patrollers quickly rode over to the accident site with rescue equipment. The group identified the victim's last seen point and a systematic probe line was set up. After one and a half hours with no results, the last seen point was

*Fig. 5.5 Middle Kootenay Pass, 89-01-04. X - deceased. M - snowmobile. The clearing for the wellsite is in the foreground.*

reassessed and a smaller group of probers searched another likely area. Within 15 minutes one of the probers struck the buried snowmobile under 30 cm of snow. It was standing on end, nose down. The probe line was re-established 10 m below the machine and continued uphill. After probing for 30 m without success, the probe line was moved to the east of the first line. Ten metres up from the snowmobile one of the probes got a hit. Shovellers started digging while the probe line continued. The probe had in fact hit the victim and he was uncovered from under 2 m of snow after being buried for 3 hours and 13 minutes.

A doctor was at the scene by this time and examined him for vital signs but could not find any. He initiated CPR and they were flown to the ski area parking lot where an ambulance brought them the rest of the way to the hospi-tal as it was too dark for the helicopter to continue flying. The victim was pronounced dead on arrival at the hospital.

Due to poor weather, avalanche dogs could not be flown to the scene earlier and only arrived just when the victim had been found.

**Source:** Westcastle Ski Patrol

**Comment:** As with many other snowmobile avalanche accidents, the party was lacking in avalanche equipment, training and information. The group chose to high-mark a slope when the avalanche danger was extreme. Also, they exposed more than one person at a time. Rescue equipment, especially transceivers, would have reduced the victim's burial time and improved the odds of a live recovery.

Two other snowmobilers died on this same slope in 1994.

---

# Thornhill Mountain near Terrace, BC

3 January 1992

- **two snowmobilers killed**
- **group lacked transceivers, probes and shovels**

| Weather Conditions at Terrace Airport Elevation 220 m, 10 km west of accident site | | | |
|---|---|---|---|
| Date 1991-92 | Max. Temp. (°C) | Min. Temp. (°C) | Precipitation (mm) |
| 12-30 | 1.9 | 0.4 | 0.1 |
| 12-31 | 1.5 | 0.0 | 25.2 |
| 01-01 | 3.6 | 0.7 | 17.6 |
| 01-02 | 2.7 | 0.2 | 8.4 |
| 01-03 | 2.2 | -0.4 | 1.4 |

On January 3rd, seven snowmobilers were riding on the north slopes of Thornhill Mountain, just southeast of Terrace, BC. The riders were each trying to ride as far up the slope—which reached 38°—as possible (high-marking). Two avalanche deposits, 1 to 2 days old, were visible on slopes adjacent to the high-marking slope.

The season in the Skeena Mountains had been warmer and wetter than average. Almost three times the normal precipitation fell in December. Between December 22nd and January 3rd, 125 mm of precipitation fell at the Terrace Airport, 1100 m below the slopes of Thornhill Mountain. During this same period, moderate or strong winds from the south had loaded north-facing slopes. On January 3rd, the tem-

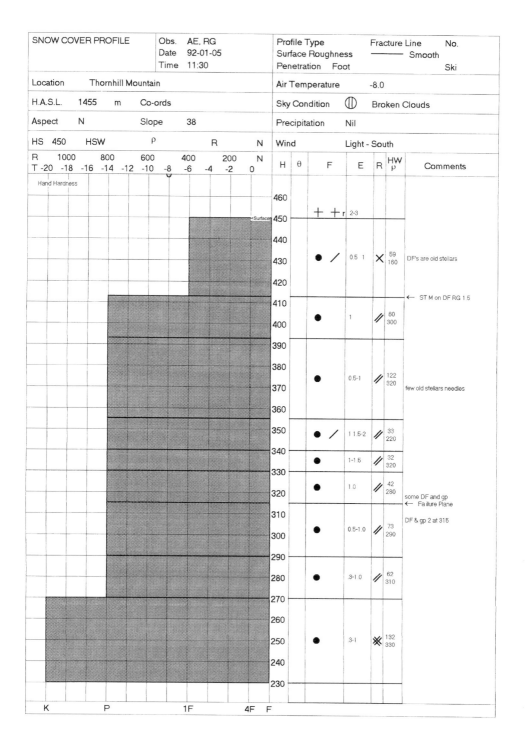

*Fig. 5.6   Fracture line profile from Thornhill Mountain observed two days after accident.*

*Fig. 5.7 Thornhill Mountain, 92-01-03. 1, 2 - locations of riders before when avalanche started. X - deceased. M - snowmobile.*

perature at the north slope was about -3°C. Strong southwest winds continued to load the slope.

At 15:15, two riders were making their last climb of the day. One was 75 m ahead and starting his descent when the slope released as a large slab avalanche. As the slab started to move, the first rider descended past the second rider whose machine was facing across the slope. The two snowmobilers were pushed off their machines and were briefly visible on the surface of the avalanche. The other riders could not see the two victims or their machines when the avalanche stopped.

The five surviving riders searched the surface of the deposit, calling for their friends and flipping over blocks of snow. After ten minutes, one went to the ridge to call for help on his radio phone but found his battery was dead. The others cut some small trees nearby to use as probes. Returning to the avalanche, they spotted one of the snowmobiles barely visible

in the deposit. As one person rode out to get help, the others dug out the machine and began to probe above it. Additional snowmobilers arrived and formed a probe line with the original group. They used the sticks to probe an area about 14 m wide around the recovered machine. At 17:30 it was getting dark and the weather was deteriorating. The four original searchers who were tired, wet and cold, left the accident site for Terrace. Seven searchers continued with wooden probes and no shovels.

In Terrace, rescue teams were being organised. Since it was too late to fly rescuers to the site, they prepared to travel by snowmobile. The first team with a RCMP dog left Terrace at 17:30. The second with additional probes and shovels left at 17:45. A storm with 70-80 km/h winds made snowmobiling—part of which was along a ridge—slow and difficult.

The first of the searchers from Terrace arrived at 19:30. A search dog arrived at 20:00 and found the second machine. At 22:25, over

seven hours after the avalanche, probers found the first body within 2 m of the first snowmobile and under 70 cm of snow. An hour later, the dog located the second body under 80 cm of snow, 37 m uphill from his machine and at the side of the deposit. Both had asphyxiated.

The 400 m-wide slab failed on a layer of graupel and partly decomposed particles. The crown varied in thickness from 60 to 135 cm and averaged 115 cm. The size 3 avalanche resulted in a 1.3 m deep deposit, 125 wide and 200 m long.

**Source:** Alan Evenchick, Regional Avalanche Technician, BC Ministry of Highways, Terrace

**Comment:** The accident party initially probed in the right area for the second victim—near his snowmobile. However, their improvised probes only penetrated about 35 cm and he was found at twice that depth. The chances of recovering both victims alive would have been much better if the snowmobilers had been equipped with, and familiar with, transceivers, shovels and probes.

The slope had been repeatedly high-marked before it released. Presumably, the victims triggered the slope from an isolated weakness or an area where the slab was thinner than average. Such events show that safety measures remain appropriate after a slope has been "tested."

Had they been high-marking one at a time, at most one rider would have been caught.

---

# Owl's Head Mountain, near Sicamous, BC

13 December 1992

- **four snowmobilers caught, one completely buried and killed**
- **no avalanche rescue equipment**
- **weak layer of facets in mid-pack**

Ten snowmobilers started their day at about 10:00 and headed into the Owl's Head Ecological Reserve south of Sicamous, British Columbia. When it came time to start heading back, the clouds were very thick in the area where they had ascended, so they decided to take an alternate route home. They rode along a ridge and then chose a 150 m-long, funnel-shaped slope to descend down into Echo Valley. They started down one after the other with some space between them. The first and second snowmobilers arrived safely at the bottom.

As in other areas of the Columbia Mountains, the Owl's Head Reserve had received relatively little snow so far that winter and the temperatures had also been unusually low. These two factors combined to produce significant faceting in the snowpack. In particular, there was a 2 cm-thick layer of very low resistance facets about 50 cm below the surface. The bowl they were heading down faced northeast, reinforcing the cold temperatures and promoting faceting more so than on southerly and westerly aspects. The funnel shape of the slope formed a terrain trap.

As the third rider neared the bottom she was hit from behind by an avalanche and was pushed along in front of it, ending up on top, a little dazed, but otherwise all right. Four of the seven riders behind her were also on the slope when it released. Two of them were carried to the left edge of the avalanche and were buried up to their chests, still standing on their machines. The other two were more to the right side and one of them hit a large rock, came off his machine, and ended up some 20 m below it, buried up to his shoulders. The other person was carried further downhill and also came off his

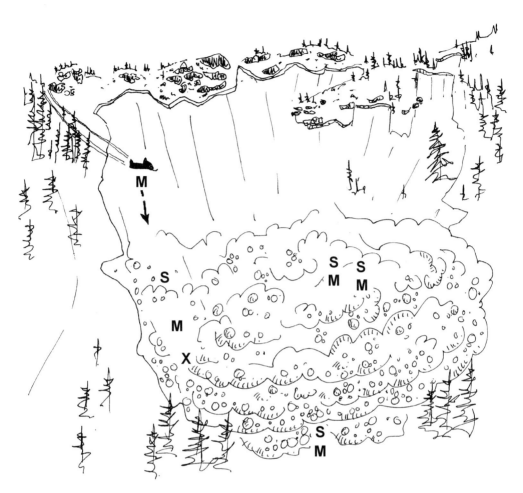

*Fig. 5.8 Owl's Head Mountain, 92-12-13. X - deceased. S - survivors. M - snowmobiles.*

machine, ending up 3 m downhill from his snowmobile and completely buried under about 1 m of snow (Fig. 5.8).

The last three snowmobilers were just about to enter the slope when they saw the avalanche go by. Once the snow stopped moving, they quickly rode down to the partially buried riders and helped them out. The three riders at the bottom also made their way back up the slope to help. When they were all together they took a head count and realised one of their party was still missing. They found the completely buried rider's snowmobile sticking out of the snow and, since they were not wearing transceivers, they attempted random digging around the machine. They also had no shovels so progress was very slow. They decided to send one person out for help — about a one-hour ride. They then broke

off a tree limb to use as a probe and continued to search around the machine and further downhill. After searching for about two hours it started to get dark. They were also becoming cold and so decided to abandon the search and get everyone out to safety. As they neared the road they met the rescue party coming in with the police and their search dog. Some of the original group refuelled and headed back up with the rescuers. Once on the site, the dog indicated an area within five minutes and they proceeded to uncover the body of the buried snowmobiler from under 110 cm of snow. The day ended at 23:00.

The following day an avalanche investigator went into the site to investigate. The size 2.5 avalanche had fractured just below some cliffs near the top of the bowl, over a width of

250 m, linking a couple of slopes. It had been constrained by the terrain as it moved downhill and near the bottom its width was greatly reduced. The group of snowmobiles had likely triggered the avalanche as they entered the slope. Their combined weight probably triggered a collapse in the soft, faceted layer in the mid-pack which, in turn, propagated towards the upper end of the slope to where the slab fractured.

**Source:** Jim Bay, Stellar Consulting Services Ltd.

**Comment:** Staying out of trouble should be the first concern. This involves terrain and snowpack analysis. Once these have been assessed, group management comes into play. If the terrain and conditions warrant it, riding down or across a slope one at a time may be a good idea. If an avalanche occurs and someone is completely buried, they must be found and uncovered as quickly as possible. After 15 minutes the odds of a live recovery have decreased to about 50%. This requires that all party members are adequately equipped, wearing avalanche transceivers and carrying probes and shovels — and that they know how to use them.

---

# Mount Skookum, near Carcross, Yukon

7 March 1993

- **one snowmobiler killed**
- **high-marking**
- **shallow snowpack - wind slab over depth hoar**

On March 7th, twelve snowmobilers made their way up above treeline and spent all morning taking runs up and down a small bowl in the Mount Skookum area near Carcross, Yukon. They made about 50 runs before lunch. After lunch all but three of them moved over to an adjacent slope. One of the three took another run up the slope and became stuck. He got off his machine to pull the skis around.

It was a cold, sunny day and the slope they were on had a classic mountain snowpack for this region. It consisted of depth hoar with a stiff wind slab at the surface. The snowpack was only about 45 cm deep and was therefore susceptible to the very cold temperatures which would change its crystalline structure and weaken it. At the base of the depth hoar was smooth rock and the concave slope steepened to almost 35° near the top. The wind slab at the surface was very hard, supporting their machines as they rode over it.

As the second snowmobiler rode up towards the stuck rider he triggered an avalanche. The stuck snowmobiler saw it fracture and attempted to run up the slope to escape. The second snowmobiler, also trying to escape, rode higher up the slope above the first rider where he triggered a second avalanche. This slide spread 100 m across the slope and right down to the rock surface underneath. It caught the first rider and his machine and carried him down-slope and completely buried him. The second snowmobiler was able to ride out to the side. The third rider at the bottom of the slope also saw it happen and attempted to ride out to the side but the avalanche caught him before he could escape; however it only partially buried him. The first rider ended up beside his machine under about 75 cm of snow.

He was not wearing an avalanche transceiver and his friends were not carrying probes or shovels, but they had noted his last seen point and therefore had a good idea where to start looking. One person was sent out for help, 3 or 4 were sent down to treeline to cut branches for probes and the rest dug with their hands

around the snowmobile. They found his foot after about ten minutes and cleared his face after another twenty minutes. It took another ten minutes to free his body. By this time he was hypothermic and showed no vital signs so they started CPR. Rescue personnel responded to the scene some time later and evacuated the snowmobiler. He was declared dead due to asphyxiation the next morning.

**Source:** Kirstie Simpson, CARDA

**Comment:** Even rudimentary stability evaluations can identify potentially dangerous slopes. The weak snowpack structure underneath the wind slab would have been quite obvious in a quick snow pit. This would have identified the slope as unstable and should have kept the snowmobilers off the slope. Even though they were able to do 50 runs on the slope in the morning without incident, the spring sunshine had warmed up the slope by early afternoon, weakening it to the point where the snowmobiles were an effective trigger.

Improvisation can only go so far. Being properly equipped and trained for the backcountry is paramount when something does go wrong. A transceiver, shovel and probe should always be carried and everyone should know how to use them.

---

# Bourne Glacier, near Revelstoke, BC

10 March 1993

- **one snowmobiler killed**
- **no transceivers or shovels**

On March 10th, eight snowmobilers were riding in the area of the Bourne Glacier, about 70 km northwest of Revelstoke, BC. At 15:30, three of the riders approached a steep east-facing chute. Two accelerated up the chute, 10 m apart, to see how far they could climb it. The first rider was turning to descend when the slope released. He tried to ride down but "could not go fast enough to get ahead of the slide" and was buried. The second was thrown from his sled and almost completely buried. The third rider was not caught.

The third rider could not see the first two and went to get the five other riders that were 500 m away. When they arrived back at the avalanche deposit, they turned off their machines and heard someone shouting. They ran towards the voice and saw the second rider's helmet and hand sticking out of the deposit. Using the belt covers from their snowmobiles as shovels, they dug out the second rider's head. He said he was "all right" so one person stayed to dig him out while the others began to search for the first rider.

They had one probe and soon struck an object about 3 m down that they believed to be the first rider's machine. After about 30 minutes of digging they uncovered his helmet. He was not breathing so they enlarged the hole so one person could give artificial respiration while held by the feet. One person went out to report the accident to the RCMP while the others continued enlarging the hole. The first rider was uncovered after a further one hour and forty-five minutes of digging. He was still on his machine with his chest pushed against the handlebars. They moved him to a flat area and attempted CPR without success. He had suffocated.

The 150 cm-thick slab released 20 m wide on a 42° slope at 2200 m above sea level. The avalanche ran down-slope for about 600 m resulting in a 20 m-deep deposit, 40 m wide, at 1900 m (Fig. 5.9).

**Source:** Report from BC Coroner's Inquiry

*Fig. 5.9 Bourne Glacier, 93-03-10. 1, 2 - locations of riders when avalanche started. X - deceased. M - snowmobile. The location of the survivor was not reported.*

**Comment:** The Coroner's report notes that "The features that are now being built into some of the machines enable the operators to access and travel in extreme avalanche terrain. Snowmobilers need to be better educated on the hazards of travelling in … avalanche terrain, as well as on search and rescue equipment and techniques."

# Oscar Creek near Ymir, BC

5 January 1994

- **one snowmobiler killed**
- **no rescue gear**
- **surface hoar**

| Date 1994 | Time | Sky, Precip. | Max. Temp. (°C) | Min. Temp. (°C) | Snowfall (cm) | Storm Snow (cm) | | Wind |
|---|---|---|---|---|---|---|---|---|
| | | | | | | | | |

| Weather Conditions at Kootenay Pass Study Plot Elevation 1775 m, 23 km SE of accident site | | | | | | | | |
|---|---|---|---|---|---|---|---|---|
| Date 1994 | Time | Sky, Precip. | Max. Temp. (°C) | Min. Temp. (°C) | Snowfall (cm) | Storm Snow (cm) | | Wind |
| 01-01 | 0600 | Obs. S 2 | -3.5 | -6.0 | 10 | 10 | | L - SW |
| 01-01 | 1505 | Obs. Nil | -3.5 | -4.5 | 3 | 13 | Cl | Calm |
| 01-02 | 0710 | Obs. S-1 | -3.0 | -5.0 | 0.1 | 0.1 | | L - W |
| 01-02 | 1500 | Obs. S-1 | -3.0 | -4.5 | 5 | 5 | | L - SW |
| 01-03 | 0700 | Bkn Nil | -3.0 | -5.0 | 5 | 10 | Cl | L - W |
| 01-03 | 1505 | Sct Nil | -4.0 | -6.0 | 0 | 0 | | Calm |
| 01-04 | 0620 | Ovc. S 2 | -1.0 | -5.5 | 7 | 7 | | L - SW |
| 01-04 | 1515 | Ovc. S 1 | -0.5 | -1.5 | 11 | 18 | | L - S |
| 01-05 | 0700 | Ovc. S-1 | -0.5 | -4.5 | 3 | 20 | | L - SE |
| 01-05 | 1440 | Ovc. S-1 | -4.0 | -4.5 | 4 | 24 | Cl | L - SE |
| 01-06 | 0715 | Sct Nil | -4.5 | -13.0 | 1 | 1 | | Calm |

On January 5th, after a day of snowmobiling, two riders were coming down the Oscar Creek logging road. Shortly after 17:00 they encountered an avalanche deposit on the road and left the road to go down around it. After they returned to the road, the first rider, Butch, began "high-marking", turning up onto the cut block above the road and back onto the road.

A prominent layer of surface hoar had formed over Christmas 1993 throughout the Interior Ranges of British Columbia. At Kootenay Pass, 26 cm of snow fell on the surface hoar from December 29th to 31st and another 49 cm in the first five days of 1994. Snowfall and winds were light on January 5th.

The second rider began to follow the first when she noticed the snow starting to move. "*I didn't see it coming. I couldn't move because there was so much snow. I couldn't see Butch anymore. The snow was starting to bury my machine and my leg. ... I pulled my leg out and the snow kept coming. I tried to stand on top of my machine to stay above the machine. ... Then everything stopped moving and it became really still.*"

The second rider shut off her machine and went ahead to where she had last seen Butch. "*I dug many holes with my bare hands, one six feet deep and in the area I had seen him last ... and none at the bottom of the avalanche where he was later found under only two feet of snow.*" She decided to go for help. "*The avalanche seemed so big it would take forever to find him.*" She dug out her machine but could not get it out of the hole. About 30-45 minutes after the avalanche, she began to walk 8 km down the road to get help.

The RCMP and a search dog arrived on the scene four hours later. The dog located the victim's body pinned under his machine which was covered by 40 cm of snow (Fig. 5.11).

The 45 cm slab failed on the layer of surface hoar that was buried December 29th. The 100 m wide slab ran down the logging cut and

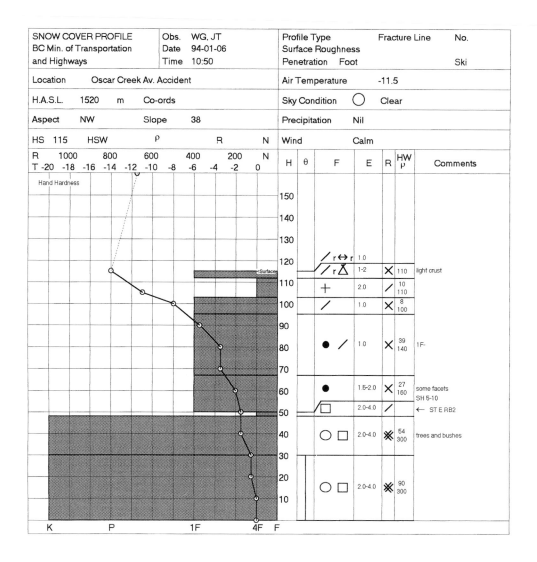

*Fig. 5.10 Fracture line profile at site of Oscar Creek accident, observed one day after avalanche, showing easy shear on surface hoar.*

over the road, depositing 200-240 cm of snow. The size 2.5 avalanche started on a 38° north-facing slope at an elevation of 1600 m. The next day investigators found a *very easy* shovel shear and a rutschblock 2 score on the surface hoar, indicating very unstable conditions.

**Source:** John Tweedy, Kootenay Pass Avalanche Technician, BC Ministry of Transportation and Highways and Tracey Telford, Salmo, BC

**Survivor's Comment:** *He died because I didn't have a [transceiver], probe and shovel. Neither did he. He died because we didn't take nine hours out of our busy schedule to take an avalanche awareness course. Now I realise the importance of equipping myself with avalanche safety knowledge and search and rescue gear. I also realise that in the end it is up to each individual to be responsible for their safety.*

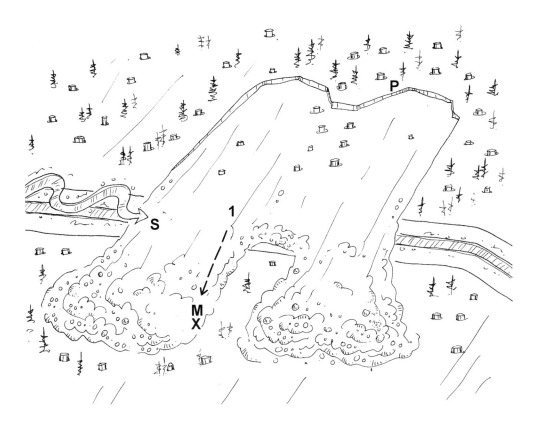

*Fig. 5.11 Oscar Creek, 94-01-05. 1 - approximate location of first rider when avalanche started.*
*X - deceased. S - survivor. M - snowmobile.*

# Middle Kootenay Pass, near Pincher Creek, Alberta

13 February 1994

- **two snowmobilers killed**
- **high avalanche danger**
- **high-marking**
- **watching from unsafe location**
- **weak faceted layer**

A group of 20 snowmobilers had spent the morning on a search and rescue mission near Pincher Creek, Alberta for three snowmobilers that had not made it back out the night before. After finding the three, who had had mechanical problems, eight of the rescue group brought them back to the trailhead while the other 12 worked on retrieving the snowmobile that had bogged down. While returning, eight of the twelve had got ahead of the rest and were waiting near an old well site. This particular spot is popular for high-marking as the clearing allows a snowmobiler to accelerate to a good speed before starting to climb the adjacent slope.

It was snowing lightly, the sky was overcast, the temperature was -3°C and a light to moderate wind was blowing out of the southwest. They had all been specifically told that there was a high avalanche danger and that high-marking or "hammer-heading" was out of the question for that day. The reason for the high danger was a weak layer of faceted wet grains in the middle of the snowpack. The top 5 cm of snowpack had been saturated by rain on December 10th and had, with subsequent very cold temperatures, been weakened by the faceting process. About 60 cm of snow had accumulated between the 10th of December and the 8th of February. In addition to the weakness, there had been a significant wind event on the 8th and 9th of February with gusts in excess of 100 km/h which had created new wind slabs that were poorly bonded to an older wind slab. Lastly, there had also been 13 cm of storm snow over the previous 48 hours.

Even after being advised of the high danger and to stay off the slope, two members of the group decided to do some high-marking anyway. Snowmobiler 1 had a run at the 35° slope and got stuck about three quarters of the way up. A few minutes later, at about 11:40, Snowmobiler 2 also sped up the slope and when he was about two thirds of the way up a size 3 avalanche released. Snowmobiler 2 was able to ride out to the side of the avalanche and escape. At the bottom of the slope the other six had seen the avalanche start and five of them managed to ride out of the path of the slide. One of them, however, was sitting on an old road directly below the slope and did not escape in time (Fig. 5.12).

The avalanche fractured right up to the ridge line and out over a width of 150 m. The slab depth was about 80 cm and it ran 100 m down the slope. The combined weight of the two

*Fig. 5.12 Middle Kootenay Pass, 94-02-13. Acceleration zone is old well site shown in foreground.*
*1 - location of stuck snowmobiler when avalanche started. 2 - direction of travel of Snowmobiler 2 riding out of avalanche. 3 - location of Snowmobiler 3 when avalanche started. X - deceased. M - snowmobiles.*

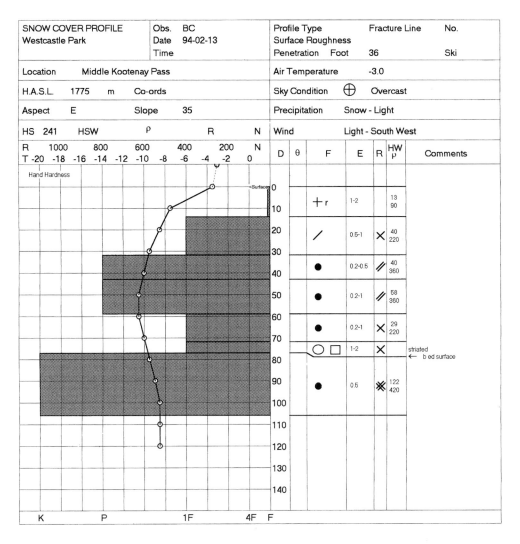

*Fig. 5.13  Fracture line profile from Middle Kootenay Pass. Total snow depth was 241 cm. Note that the striated layer (72-77 cm) above the bed surface was a rain saturated snow layer from 93-12-10. The faceting appeared more advanced in the upper portion of this layer.*

snowmobilers and their machines had overloaded the weak layer of faceted wet grains. The deepest part of the deposit was about 6 m.

Snowmobiler 1 was carried all the way back down to where the slope flattened out and was buried under 3 m of snow. His snowmobile ended up on top of the deposit about 20 m further down the slope. Snowmobiler 3, the person at the bottom, was buried under 2 m of snow and about 3 m downhill from his snowmobile.

All members of the group had transceivers, probes and shovels, so they were able to locate the victims fairly quickly. Rescue personnel from the nearby ski hill had been contacted by radio and they arrived on the scene at 11:55.

Snowmobiler 3 was the first to be uncovered after being buried for 25 minutes. He was not breathing nor did he have a pulse so CPR was started. Snowmobiler 1 was uncovered at 12:20 after being under the snow for 40 minutes. He did not show any vital signs either. By this time a doctor was on the scene and pronounced him dead. CPR on Snowmobiler 3 was stopped at 14:00 when the doctor pronounced him dead as well.

One of the original search party afterwards questioned, "Why did they do it? We were told not to."

**Source:** Brian Cusack, Westcastle Ski Area

**Comment:** High-marking at times of high avalanche danger is extremely dangerous. The terrain the snowmobilers chose was not appropriate for the conditions. A slope that is already fragile will only allow a certain amount of additional load before it releases. While one snowmobile and rider may be tolerable, any additional load will increase the chances of it avalanching.

It is also important that when stopping in avalanche terrain, people position themselves in areas not exposed to avalanches from above.

Another snowmobiler died on this same slope in 1989.

---

# Hasler Creek, near Chetwynd, BC

13 February 1994

## • one snowmobiler buried and killed

Two snowmobilers were riding in the Hasler Creek area near Chetwynd, British Columbia. At one point they needed to traverse across a steep avalanche chute and the first one entered the slope about three quarters of the way down. As he was in the chute an avalanche released near the top of the slope to a depth of 1.5 m and a width of 100 m. It carried the snowmobiler and his machine down to the trees at the bottom of the chute, pushing the snowmobile up against a tree and burying the rider.

No one at the scene had any avalanche training and it was not until more than two hours later that the police and their search dog arrived. There had been about 10 other snowmobilers in the area and they had started a search with probes and had left pieces of flagging tape at the sites they had probed. These threw off the dog and needed to be cleared off the debris. After 50 minutes the search dog indicated a spot about 10 m from the snowmobile. The victim's location was then pin-pointed by probe and he was shovelled out. He did not have any vital signs, having been buried at least three hours.

**Comment:** It was fortunate that both riders were not on the slope at the same time. By crossing suspect slopes one at a time the number of people exposed to danger is minimised.

Rescue equipment and training are two requirements when travelling in the backcountry. Even if it is not your party that gets into trouble, being able to help those in need is part of everyone's responsibility out there.

# Coyote Creek, southern Rockies

5 March 1994

- **one snowmobiler buried**
- **successful rescue**
- **basic awareness training**

A group of 15 snowmobilers was spending the day in the Coyote Creek area of the Rockies, in southeastern British Columbia. They had observed two avalanches during the day but continued up to Wildhorse Summit. At 15:00 one of the snowmobilers rode up an open slope and got stuck about half way up.

It was a warm sunny day on the south-facing slope, the temperature was well above zero and the rocky outcrops at the top had been heating up.

As his machine bogged down, a size 3 avalanche released out of the rocks above and carried him 200 m down the slope. The fracture line was about 1 m deep and extended for 300 m across the slope. The avalanche ran about 400 m.

The other 14 snowmobilers at the bottom saw the avalanche start and quickly rode out of its path. Although they were not equipped with avalanche rescue gear, they had attended a basic avalanche awareness course and therefore knew some of the things to do. One rider kept an eye on the victim to establish his last seen point. When the snow stopped moving he noted the spot and the group then cut sticks from nearby trees to probe the area. After 10 minutes they had found and uncovered the unconscious victim from under 1 m of snow. He was 2 m away from his machine. He recovered.

**Source:** Gordon Burns, Mountain Magic Ventures

**Comment:** The basic avalanche training taken by his friends probably saved the victim's life. However, with the training they should not have ended up in this situation in the first place. Natural avalanches are an indication of instability and should be noted with respect. Sunny warm days will affect south-facing slopes the most, especially in the afternoon and in areas where the snow comes in contact with exposed rocks.

# Bruce Creek, Purcell Mountains

26 February 1995

- **one snowmobiler killed**
- **terrain trap**

On February 26th, seven snowmobilers made their way to the upper reaches of Bruce Creek in the Purcell mountains of southeastern British Columbia. On their way back down, at about 14:30, they were working their way through a tight canyon, riding along one side with a large avalanche slope looming above them.

Many large avalanches could be seen that day in the surrounding mountains. The snowpack had a layer of storm snow with a tenuous bond to the older snow underneath in some areas. The southeast-facing slope they were riding on rose at an angle of 35° for over 300 m above them.

They rode up and along the side of this slope, above a lower angled portion which abruptly changed to 15° just meters below them. As the third snowmobiler rode over part of this slope he triggered a size 2.5 avalanche that was only a small part at the bottom of the much larger slope. Had the whole 300 m slope released, the consequences would have been much worse. The slab broke out over an area of 75 m wide by 50 m high by 60 cm deep. The rider was carried down onto the lower angled terrain and flipped upside down, with his machine ending up above him as if he were still sitting on it. The debris from the avalanche quickly piled up deeply on the relatively flat part of the slope and buried him under 2 m of snow.

The first and second snowmobilers did not even realise that the avalanche had occurred, but the members behind were able to respond quickly. All of the rescuers had transceivers, shovels and probes. Unfortunately the victim was the only one in the party not wearing a transceiver. Nevertheless, he was still found within six minutes. The rescuers dug him out and started CPR and after 20 minutes he started breathing on his own, but he was still unconscious and his pulse was erratic. A little while later he was evacuated by helicopter to the local hospital and then onwards to a Calgary hospital. He never regained consciousness and was taken off life support four days later.

**Source:** Rod Gibbons

**Comment:** The noise of snowmobiles combined with the muffling effect of the helmet make it difficult to hear much else. This makes it even more important to stay aware of what is happening around you. Constant visual checks are necessary when in avalanche terrain as you may not be able to hear the sound of the avalanche or the cries for help from your partners.

Terrain traps can sometimes take less obvious forms, as in the case above. An abrupt change from a steep to a shallow slope will allow the debris to accumulate much deeper at the transition than if the slope had a more gradual run-out. Careful terrain analysis is a key element in staying out of trouble.

---

# Broadview Mountain, Kakwa Recreation Area

5 March 1995

- **one snowmobiler killed**
- **no transceivers**
- **persistent weak layer in old snow**

On March 5th, five snowmobilers were riding in Kakwa Recreation Area near Cecilia Lake, about 75 km north of McBride, BC. To get to an area they had not been before, they wanted to climb a southeast-facing slope on Mt. Broadview. Two riders stopped near a small group of trees while the other three drove their sleds up the slope. The snowmobiler on the right was in the middle of the slope when his machine got stuck. He got off his sled and was hit by an avalanche. The other two riders on the slope got away from the slide. The snowmobilers near the trees saw the victim appear and then disappear in the flowing avalanche. After the avalanche stopped, the four remaining snowmobilers looked over the deposit, but could only see the victim's snowmobile.

One rider went for help and encountered another group of snowmobilers that had a cellular phone. Using the phone, they relayed a message to the RCMP in McBride. The two groups continued to search the deposit.

*Fig. 5.14 Broadview Mountain, 95-03-05. L - last seen point. X - deceased. M - snowmobile. Trent Smith photo.*

RCMP searchers, Jasper Park Wardens, a Parks Canada search dog and a CARDA search dog all arrived on the scene the next morning. After an hour and twenty minutes, a search dog found the victim's body under 2 m of snow, within 20 m of his snowmobile (Fig. 5.14).

The 250 m-wide slab reached a maximum thickness of 2 m on the lee slope to the west of the victim's route. The size 2.5 avalanche resulted in a 280 m-wide deposit, 2-3 m deep.

**Source:** Jasper Park Warden Service

**Comment:** The snowmobilers chose to climb an obviously wind-loaded slope three at a time, perhaps misled by the lack of recent avalanches in the area.

The group was not equipped to do avalanche rescue. They had no transceivers or probes and had left their shovels at their camp. Transceivers would have made the search much faster and increased the probability of a live recovery.

After the search was completed, rescuers observed three snow profiles near the crown fracture and one near the toe of the deposit. Only the profile below the deposit showed a pronounced weakness at the level of the shear failure that released the slab. At this site, both compression tests resulted in *easy* failures in a thin layer of 2 mm surface hoar crystals. Apparently, the snow lower on the slope was less stable—and more sensitive to triggers—than the snow remaining above the crown.

# Doctor Creek, Purcell Mountains

19 March 1995

- **two snowmobilers killed**
- **high-marking trigger**
- **unsafe rest spot**

It was just after noon on March 19th when 14 snowmobilers arrived on a slope at treeline, near Doctor Creek in the Purcell Mountains of southeastern British Columbia. Part-way up on the west side of the slope was a small bench and 11 riders headed towards it to break for lunch. One snowmobiler was at the bottom of the slope and two others rode over to the east side of the slope to do some high-marking. The group of 11 arrived at the bench and started shutting down their machines.

The slope was a classic avalanche slope. The ridge top was scoured down to bare rock and a lot of snow had been transported onto the lee side, loading it with a deep pillow of snow. The slope faced southeast and was quite steep, reaching 40°, except for the flatter bench where the large group had stopped.

As the group was shutting down, the two on the east side had just done a high turn and were heading back down when they triggered a size 2.5 avalanche. It fractured behind them

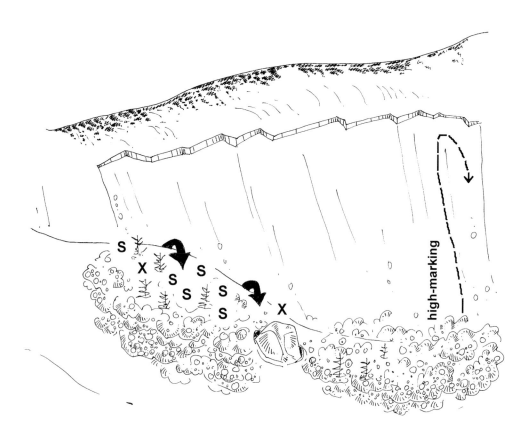

*Fig. 5.15 Doctor Creek, 95-03-19. X - deceased. S - the survivors were spread out along the bench where they had stopped for lunch.*

and zippered out over a width of 200 m, over to and above the group of 11 on the west side of the slope. The slab was up to 1.5 m thick and slid right to ground, running 100 m down the slope. The two on the east side were able to outrun it by speeding down the slope. However, four of the others ended up partially buried and four more were completely buried.

The remaining six snowmobilers spent the next one and a half hours searching for and uncovering the buried members of their group. Some had transceivers and some did not. They used probes and shovels. They also sent out someone to get help. One of the partially buried snowmobilers was able to get free and then rescue his buried son using his transceiver. In the end, two people were injured and two were dead. Of these latter two, one had a transceiver and one did not. Both were buried under 1 m of snow.

**Source:** Rod Gibbons

**Comment:** Rest spots should be assessed carefully for their exposure to avalanches, keeping in mind that avalanches can and do fracture out over large distances. A slope should be thought of as a single unit where an action on one part of it can affect the whole.

---

# Telkwa Range, near Houston, BC

19 March 1995

- **one snowmobiler buried and killed**
- **high-marking**
- **no avalanche rescue equipment**

On the afternoon of the 19th, four snowmobilers were high-marking on a slope in the Telkwa Mountains south of Houston, British Columbia. They had done a number of runs at the slope and their tracks covered a good portion of it. While the others watched from below, one of the snowmobilers took a line to the west of a 20 m-high rock spur. He rode up a steep 40° slope and was just about to reach the slightly flatter terrain above it. This would put him higher than any of the existing tracks.

The slope faced southeast and was only about 115 m high. The snowpack was well consolidated, fairly hard but relatively shallow and had therefore undergone some faceting throughout its depth. One consistent but hard shear did exist down about 90 cm. This was a weak layer that had probably formed during a cold period in early March. The weakness, however, was well bridged by the stiff snow above and did not react to ski-cutting.

As the snowmobiler started to top out above the steep section, he was higher on the slope and closer to the rocks than any of the previous tracks. Apparently, he hit a sensitive spot and the weight and motion of the snowmobile became too much for the weak layer in the midpack and he triggered a size 3 avalanche. His friends could see him for a few moments as the snow started moving but then the billowing powder cloud obscured everything. The avalanche carried him and his machine down the slope to a point where the terrain started to flatten out. The snowmobile ended up on the surface, but the rider was buried under 2 m of snow. The entire slope had released, going right down to ground near the rocks, but had generally released at the 90 cm depth of the weak faceted layer (Fig. 5.16).

Nobody in the group had any avalanche training nor did they carry transceivers, shovels or probes. They searched the deposit when

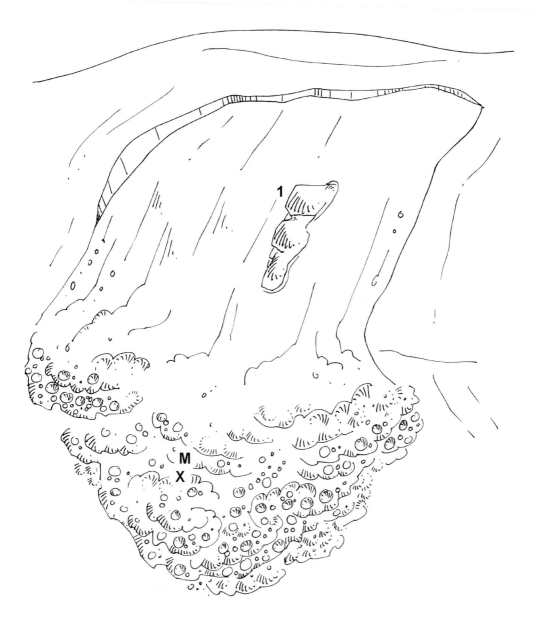

*Fig. 5.16 Telkwa Range, 95-03-19. 1 - location of snowmobiler when avalanche started. X - location of fatal burial. M - snowmobile.*

the snow had stopped moving but could only find the overturned snowmobile, some 50 m from the toe of the deposit. One of them went for help while the other two continued searching. The time was 16:30.

Three hours later, members of Bulkley Valley Search and Rescue arrived and organised a probe line. A police officer and his avalanche dog were also at the scene, but gasoline had spilt out of the victim's snowmobile and this

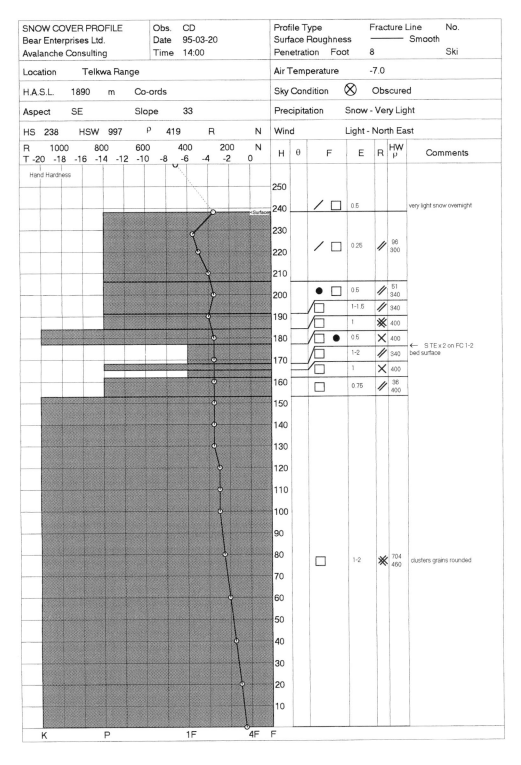

*Fig. 5.17   Fracture line profile for the Telkwa Range accident. Profile was done one day later.*

kept the dog from being able to pick up any scent. The probe line was set up starting at the toe of the deposit, to work its way uphill past the snowmobile. As avalanche victims are often found near their machines, two random probers checked the area around the snowmobile. At 20:10 one of these two got a strike. While the probe line continued, the snowmobile was moved and they started digging along the probe. At 20:30 they had uncovered the victim's face but there was no sign of life. They excavated him and started CPR but he was already cold and there had been no breathing space around his face. Unfortunately, he did not recover.

**Source:** Christoph Dietzfelbinger, Bear Enterprises Ltd.

**Comment:** The snowpack depth near rock outcrops is often shallower and weaker than the rest of the slope. Air pockets form around rocks and can accelerate the faceting process of cold temperatures to create weak, sensitive points.

Being prepared for an avalanche rescue in the backcountry is a question of responsibility. The survivors of an accident party are the only real chance the buried victims have for getting out alive. Even the fastest organised rescue will generally take longer to be alerted and respond than the buried victim has time to live (more than 30 minutes for survival is unusual). Backcountry users should always carry transceivers, shovels and probes and know how to use them.

# Sawtooth Mountain, Baffin Island

12 November 1995

- **one snowmobiler killed**
- **wind-loaded roll**
- **no transceivers**

At Sawtooth Mountain near Clyde River, the weather was good on November 12th. The clouds were scattered, there was no wind and the air warmed to -5°C. At 14:00, three snowmobilers were on the west shoulder of the mountain. One snowmobiler who had stopped his sled on a 35° wind-loaded slope was struck and buried by a size 3 avalanche.

The other two riders began to probe the deposit since none of them had transceivers. Word of the accident reached the town of Clyde River, and "a trail of [snowmobile] lights wound their way over rocks and drifts to the site." While some people probed the deposit, others set up generators and lights. The victim's body was found at 22:00 under 2 m of snow.

The 300 m-wide dry slab averaged 150 cm in thickness. It released on an east-facing slope at an elevation of 600 m.

**Source:** Mark Shubin

**Comment:** Transceivers would have permitted a faster search. However, it is not known if the victim died from asphyxia or trauma.

Wind-blown snow builds wind slabs on lee slopes such as this one. This snowmobiler stopped and was caught on a wind-loaded slope.

# Chapter 6

# Hiking and Climbing Accidents

## Mt. Allan, Kananaskis Country

9 October 1985

- **a hunter, his guide and two horses caught**
- **one horse killed**

On October 9th, two hunters shot an elk in the east-facing gully immediately south of the Nakiska Ski Area in Kananaskis Country, Alberta. They took their horses up to the dead elk, observing several small avalanches. While quartering the elk at about 16:00, a slab avalanche released above them in the gully. They scrambled to the side of the gully and hung onto willow bushes as the avalanche brushed by them. The avalanche carried the horses 100 m down the gully.

Descending to the deposit, the hunters and guide saw the ears of one horse sticking through the snow. They quickly dug out around the head and found the horse alive. They continued to dig the heavy moist snow out from around the

horse's chest. After dark, they left the horse buried to its belly and hiked down to the valley to report the accident.

At dawn the next day, they returned to the accident site with a helicopter. Using lines from the helicopter, they lifted the horse from the deposit and moved it to ground where it could stand. The other horse, when found, had its head under its body and was dead.

The size 2 avalanche started as a 30 cm moist slab, 100 m wide. The slab failed in a softer layer next to the ground and slid on long grass. The avalanche started on 35° slopes and ran down the gully for 400 m (Fig. 6.1).

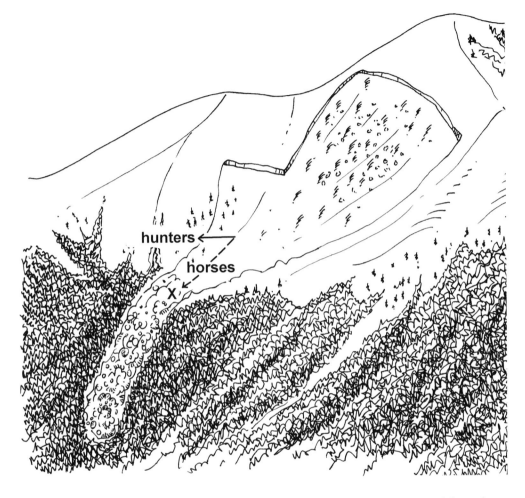

*Fig. 6.1 Mt. Allan, 85-10-09. Hunters fled to side of the slope and the horses were carried down-slope. X - location of dead horse.*

**Source:** George Field and Rod Jaeger, Kananaskis Country

**Comment:** Kananaskis country staff report that there was no evidence of other similar avalanches. They suspect that a temperature rise on October 9th contributed to the avalanche.

# Mt. Bryce, Jasper National Park

14 June 1987

- **three climbers killed**
- **cornice fall**

On June 13th, four climbers left the Icefields Parkway between Banff and Jasper and ascended the Athabasca Glacier. They camped above the third icefall on the glacier. About 11:30 the next morning, they travelled south across the Columbia Icefields to Mt. Bryce. While approaching the mountain in the afternoon, they noticed cornices breaking off.

Early in the evening, the two rope-teams ascended an hourglass-shaped couloir on the east side of the northeast ridge. At 20:30, a

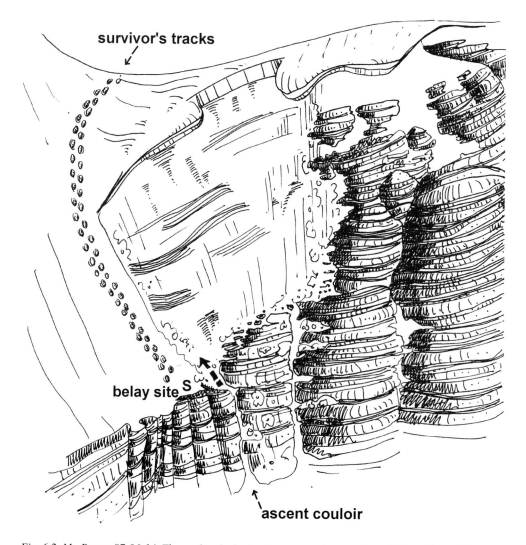

*Fig. 6.2 Mt. Bryce, 87-06-14. The avalanche broke the ropes and swept three climbers down the couloir. S - survivor at belay site.*

cornice fell above the couloir and triggered a slab avalanche. The avalanche passed the leading climber who was belaying from a buttress bordering the couloir, broke the 9 mm rope and swept the other three climbers 150 m down to the bottom of the couloir. The lead climber could see one of his three partners partly buried by the deposit. However, he felt that climbing down the couloir would be too difficult since the avalanche had scoured it down to glacier ice.

The lead climber descended the opposite side of the northeast ridge and continued down into the Bush River in British Columbia. Fourteen hours after the accident, he was picked up by a logging truck that took him to Golden where he reported the accident. Jasper Park Wardens went to the northeast ridge of Mt. Bryce with avalanche dogs and found all three victims. Two were buried under 1-1.5 m of snow. All three had suffocated in moist snow.

The crown of the slab avalanche was 1.5 m thick and ran 300 m along the slope.

**Source:** Jasper Park Warden Service

**Comment:** Avalanche prone terrain is a part of many snow and ice climbs. However, the four climbers were in the steep couloir while it was still warm. They entered the cornice-topped couloir after observing cornices falling.

The lead climber's belay stance at the side of the couloir was well chosen since the avalanche missed him.

Both 9 mm ropes broke between the climbers in the couloir, indicating the severe forces caused by the avalanche. The belayer's anchor consisted of two buried ice axes which withstood the forces. Ironically, a more experienced mountaineer might have considered one buried axe to be adequate, and would likely have been carried down-slope.

# Mt. Robson, Mt. Robson Provincial Park

1 August 1987

- **one climber killed**
- **high winds, blowing snow, poor visibility**

Two experienced climbers started up the North Face of Mt. Robson on July 28th. Due to high winds and blowing snow, they bivouacked on the face. They reached the top of the face the next day and bivouacked on the traverse to the summit. On the 30th, they bivouacked on the peak. While blasted by strong winds and blowing snow, they descended to the Kain Face, making their fourth bivouac on a plateau below the face. On August 1st, they traversed above an ice wall, looking for a rappel site where their rope would reach the bottom. While traversing unroped, they were hit by an avalanche and pushed over the ice wall onto the slope below.

The climber that stopped higher in the deposit suffered serious injuries. He was able to dig himself out before falling unconscious.

When he regained consciousness, he crawled to his partner but was unable to resuscitate him. He remained there, unable to move.

After they were notified of the overdue climbers, Jasper Park Wardens searched the mountain by helicopter on August 3rd. Seeing tracks traversing the Robson Glacier, they investigated. Although the tracks proved to be those of a wolverine, they followed them and then saw the lone survivor waving from the edge of an icefall bordering the main valley. It appears that the wolverine may have smelled the dead climber and was attempting to reach the site. Wardens evacuated the surviving climber and his partner's body.

**Source:** Jasper Park Warden Service

**Comment:** Risks are part of serious climbs such as this traverse of Mt. Robson. Unfortunately, the strong winds and blowing snow formed numerous winds slabs, some of which released as avalanches. Poor visibility made route selection on the descent particularly difficult.

# Shawinigan, Quebec

13 February 1988

- **two young girls buried, one killed**
- **long survival time**
- **small slope**

On February 13th near the city of Shawinigan, Quebec, two 13-year-old girls climbed up a small, snow covered, sand hill to slide back down. When they were about half way up they triggered an avalanche. The slide was only 20 m long by several metres wide but it buried both girls under 175 cm of snow.

Some other girls who were with them witnessed the avalanche and ran to get help from local residents. The two girls had been buried for almost 2 hours when one of the rescuers located them using a probe. They were quickly dug out and taken to a hospital. One died a few hours after being admitted while the other survived with only minor injuries.

**Comment:** It is unusual for anyone to survive such a long burial time. An air pocket can vastly extend the survival time. Since the avalanche did not run very far, the girl that survived may have benefited from an air pocket.

# Fossil Mountain, Banff National Park

20 February 1988

- **two climbers killed**
- **cross-loaded gully**
- **high avalanche hazard**

| | Weather Conditions at Temple Research Station 2000 m above sea level, 7.5 km SW of accident site | | | | |
|---|---|---|---|---|---|
| Date 1988 | Max. Temp. (°C) | Min. Temp. (°C) | Snowfall (cm) | Snowpack (cm) | Wind (km/h) |
| 02-17 | -3.5 | -8.0 | 1 | 82 | 27 - W |
| 02-18 | -4.0 | -12.5 | 0.1 | 80 | 50 - W |
| 02-19 | 1.5 | -5.5 | 0 | 80 | 45 - W |
| 02-20 | 3.0 | -2.0 | 0 | 78 | 50 - W |

On February 20th, two experienced mountaineers left the Lake Louise Ski Area and toured northeast to Fossil Mountain. Strong winds blew from the west, cross-loading the

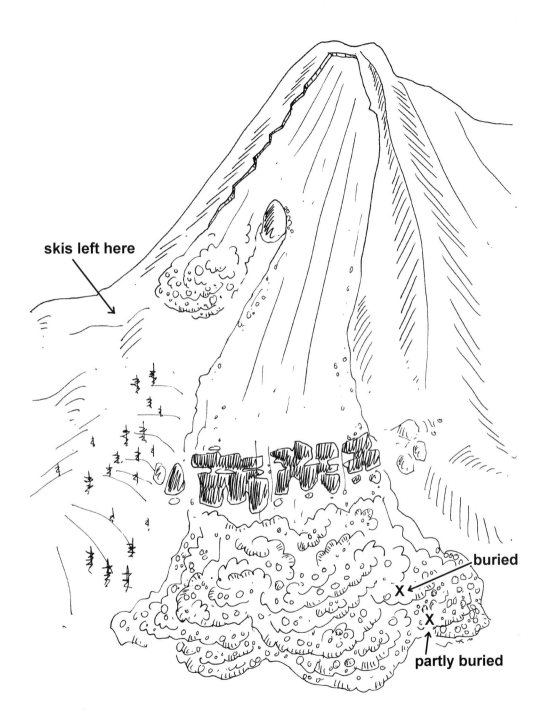

skis left here

buried

partly buried

*Fig. 6.3  Fossil Mountain, 88-02-20. The locations of the climbers when the avalanche started is not known. X - deceased.*

main gully on the south side of the mountain. About 50 m above Deception Pass, they left their skis and ascended on foot. Rescuers believe they were in the gully near the summit of Fossil Mountain when they triggered a large size 3 slab avalanche. It carried them down to 2225 m, completely burying one and partly burying the other (Fig. 6.3).

At midnight, the Banff Park Wardens were notified that the two climbers were overdue. Early the next day, people at Skoki Lodge reported having seen a large avalanche on the south side of Fossil Mountain at 13:30 the previous day. Wardens and two search dogs flew to the deposit in a helicopter. They found the first victim, partly exposed but with his head buried, facing upwards in the deposit. After an hour of searching, a dog found the second victim under 1.5 m of snow, 75 m above his partner. Neither had transceivers. Both had asphyxiated.

The slab was 1 m thick at the crown and 50 cm thick along much of the flanks. The deposit was 250 m wide, 300 m along the slope and had an average depth of 2 m.

**Source:** Banff Park Warden Service

**Comment:** Although experienced, apparently the two climbers overlooked or ignored the posted avalanche hazard which was *high,* the strong west winds and the obviously cross-loaded gully.

# Extra Light, Yoho National Park

28 December 1988

- **one ice climber killed**
- **danger from above**

On December 28th, two ice climbers decided to do a climb called "Extra Light". They started walking from Field, British Columbia, and headed east along the railway tracks below Mount Stephen and then up a trail to the base of the frozen waterfall. This area is very popular with ice climbers, with many options close by and easy access. They started climbing the first pitch of near vertical ice, unroped.

At about 14:00 the leading climber had just reached a snow and ice ramp at the top of the first pitch. Moments later he either saw or heard an avalanche coming down towards them. He yelled *"avalanche"* but was unable to get out of the way in time. The size 2 avalanche started on a snowfield on the steep slopes above and then ran down the avalanche path and over the frozen waterfall. The second climber was still on the steep part of the climb and could not see his partner, but seconds later he was hit by the avalanche, pulled off the ice and ended up partially buried in the middle of the deposit, at the base of the climb. He had a broken ankle and chest injuries. The snow set up very hard around him and it took him 45 minutes to dig himself out. He could not see his partner who must have been carried down as well, nor could he find him because neither of them were wearing transceivers and they had no probes along. Had they been roped together the survivor might have been able to follow the rope to his buried partner.

Unable to walk on his broken ankle, the climber crawled for over 2 hours down the trail to the train tracks and started towards Field. At about 17:15 a train came by and took him into town. They contacted the police and the climber was taken to the hospital in Banff by ambulance.

At 18:00 the Yoho National Park wardens were notified and a rescue was started for the other climber. They reached the scene at 20:00 and started to randomly probe the deposit. Meanwhile an avalanche dog and handler were on route. A second rescue party from Banff Park

arrived and a coarse probe line was started. The mixed ice and snow in the deposit was extremely hard and made probing very difficult. They kept probing until 22:00 when the avalanche dog and handler arrived. In just over two minutes the dog indicated a spot and the body of the climber was found. He had died of suffocation, but had also sustained serious injuries during his fall. Minutes after the body had been excavated a second small avalanche come down the path and dusted the rescuers, so they quickly moved out of danger and took the body to a staging area.

**Source:** Terry Willis, Yoho National Park

**Comment:** The avalanche danger for Yoho Park was generally moderate, but above the ice climb the wind-loaded lee slopes and gullies were exhibiting a higher danger. An awareness of what is happening above a climb becomes paramount when the intention is to spend so much time on a frozen waterfall which will often be in, or make up, an avalanche path.

Ice climbers must often assess the stability of slopes above ice climbs without being able to access and test the slopes. They must also carry the basic avalanche equipment needed to conduct self rescue.

---

# Hartly Creek, near Golden, BC

22 February 1990

- **solo ice-climber on snowshoes killed**
- **terrain trap**

Just after noon, an ice-climber left the trailhead to snowshoe up Hartly Creek, near Golden, British Columbia, on his way to climb a frozen waterfall.

It had started snowing two days earlier and the previous day it had snowed over 30 cm with moderate to strong southerly winds. On this day it was still snowing and windy but the temperature was climbing above 0°C. A neighbour had warned him about the warm temperatures and associated dangers in the narrow canyon.

At 13:00, as he was going through an extremely dangerous point in the creek where two narrow gullies intersect it, one of them avalanched. The starting zone was a steep rocky area above the 31° gully. The opposite gully was even steeper but it did not slide. The canyon was only 1 m wide at this point and did not offer any escape routes. He was caught by the avalanche and completely buried.

The victim's wife reported him missing in the evening and then went with a friend to the canyon. There they found the slide deposit and started searching. Organised rescue arrived at 21:05 when a local park warden and his avalanche dog reached the site. The threat of another avalanche from the opposite gully was very real, so the number of people searching was minimised. After clearing the searchers' articles off the deposit, the dog immediately indicated a spot and the warden hit the victim on his second probe. The victim was dug out from under about 1.5 m of snow, but due to his long burial time he was already dead.

**Source:** Gord Peyto, Glacier National Park

**Comment:** Terrain traps can come in various shapes and sizes. Any location that does not offer an escape route and/or will increase the depth of a deposit should be avoided if possible. If such an area must be travelled through, sufficient spacing and spotters should be used.

# Mt. Cascade, Banff National Park

20 April 1990

- **wet avalanche hits three hikers**
- **one hiker carried over cliffs**

Prominent gullies are set in the south face of Cascade Mountain near Banff. Snow in bowls above these gullies sometimes avalanches down them and over the cliffs. One of these gullies forms the Cascade Waterfall, which is a popular ice climb in winter. Little ice remained on this south face in April 1990.

On the 20th, three young men with little mountain experience scrambled up a canyon east of Cascade Waterfall. They ascended over several avalanche deposits that filled the gully. It started to drizzle. At about 500 m up the mountainside they traversed west above a cliff to find a easier route down to the valley. While about 70 m above the cliff, a large wet avalanche from the bowl above Cascade Waterfall hit them. One man held onto a boulder. Another was pushed to the edge of the cliff where he "clawed at the ground" to hang on. The third hiker was flushed over a 75 m-high cliff, over several 10 to 40 m cliffs and down the slope for 300 m (Fig. 6.5). He was partly buried in the wet deposit. Although he had serious internal injuries, a cracked pelvis, dislocated hip, cuts and bruises, rescuers are certain that he would not have survived such a fall without the cushioning effect of the wet avalanche. The other men suffered only cuts and bruises.

The avalanche was observed by several drivers on the Trans-Canada Highway including an off-duty warden. Banff Park Wardens organised the rescue. All three men were slung off the mountainside by helicopter.

**Source:** Banff Park Warden Service

**Comment:** When high on a mountain side, it can be difficult to pick a good route down since cliffs may be hidden from view. In this case, the hikers could not see the main cliff of the Cascade Waterfall from their traverse. Descent routes and alternatives should be planned in advance. The cliffs below and the avalanche bowl above the gully can be easily seen from the valley.

Although gullies often provide easier hiking or climbing than adjacent slopes, they funnel avalanches and rockfall, increasing the hazard.

Rain often reduces the stability of the snowpack, resulting in wet avalanches.

On rare occasions such as this incident and that of the helicopter crash on February 11th, 1978 reported in Volume 3 (Schaerer, 1987), the cushioning effect of avalanches reduces injuries.

*Fig. 6.4 The spring accident prompted the installation of this warning sign. Tim Auger photo.*

*Fig. 6.5  Cascade Mountain, 90-04-20. The waterfall was not frozen at the time of the accident. Bruce Jamieson photo.*

# Twin Falls, near Smithers, BC

27 November 1991

- **six ice climbers involved, one killed**
- **weather significantly different up high**
- **terrain trap**

On the morning of November 27th, a group of seven ice-climbers made their way up the first 25 m of low-angled ice on the right arm of Twin Falls near Smithers, British Columbia. From about 11:00 until 14:00 they practised placing anchors as well as rope systems for raising and lowering victims. They then decided to climb further up the grade 3 ice. At 16:00 they started to descend from the second belay station, one rope length above the first station they had used for the practice session. One of the members reached the bottom at 16:15 and left the scene to return to Smithers. The remaining six climbers were still on the ice and descending slowly due to the large group size. At approximately 17:00 three climbers were at the top belay station and the three others at the lower station. It was dark by this time.

The group had discussed the potential of avalanches that morning before leaving on their outing and had decided that the danger was negligible. The weather down where they were climbing was fairly constant throughout the day with light winds and cool temperatures. However, high on the steep slopes above them a strong wind was blowing from the west, cross-loading the southeast-facing slopes. The temperature was also increasing as the day progressed and reached a maximum at 16:00. The climbers experienced periods of spindrift during the day. This is often associated with wind loading higher up.

The frozen waterfall they were on drains the Hudson's Bay Glacier which is relatively low-angled (Fig. 6.6). However, the southeast-facing slope above the climbers looms some 1200 m higher up at an angle of 50 to 60° and includes 35 separate start zones.

At about 17:00 a small avalanche came down the chute but only one of the people at the upper belay station was affected. He was cut on the face by a piece of ice. They continued rappelling and at 17:20 Climbers 1 and 2 were at the upper belay station, Climbers 3, 4 and 5 were at the lower one and Climber 6 was halfway down to the bottom. It was then that a second, larger avalanche swept over the group. It was only a size 1 but it immediately dislodged Climber 6. The three climbers at the lower station were attached to their anchor but it failed and they too were carried down. The two climbers at the upper station were protected by a bulge in the ice above them and were left unaffected. After the avalanche had stopped there were four climbers at the bottom of the fozen waterfall: Climber 6 ended up on the surface, Climbers 3 and 4 were partially buried right-side-up and Climber 5 was partially buried, head down, with his feet sticking out.

Climber 6, a medical doctor, quickly freed Climber 4 and then cleared the snow from Climber 3's face. Climbers 4 and 6 then started digging out Climber 5. The snow was very dense and it took them 15 minutes to do so. When they got him out he had no vital signs and CPR was initiated. They had been doing CPR for 15 minutes when a third, smaller avalanche came down. They then decided to free Climber 3 and carry him and Climber 5 to a safer location. Climber 6 then radioed the nearby hospital for rescue assistance. When Climbers 1 and 2 got down everyone moved to a safe location south of the falls. In the end Climber 1 was uninjured, Climber 2 had a cut on his face from the first avalanche, Climber 3 had a fractured leg and dislocated elbow, Climber 4 has some bruises, Climber 6 had a fractured nose and Climber 5 did not survive.

**Source:** Ross Cloutier

**Comment:** Waterfalls, by their very nature, often form the track of an avalanche. They can also act as funnels, creating a terrain trap if an avalanche does come down. When on such an ice climb, it is best to limit the amount of time spent on the climb and to be very aware of what is happening above. Even if the start zones

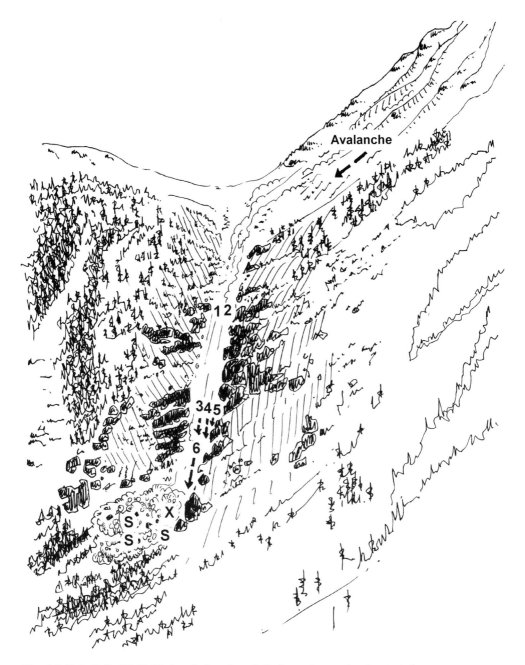

*Fig. 6.6 Twin Falls, 91-11-27. 1 to 6 - location of climbers when avalanche started.*
*X - deceased. S - survivors.*

above cannot be seen, clues of wind transport on the surrounding peaks should be noted, as well as more obvious clues such as spindrift.

A reliable anchor is also paramount, not just for safety while climbing, but also in the case of an avalanche. In the event of a small avalanche a sound anchor should reduce the chance of the belayer and/or climber being carried down.

---

# Silk Tassel, Yoho National Park

26 February 1992

- **two ice climbers partially buried, one killed**
- **high avalanche danger**
- **no rescue gear**

Four ice climbers made their way up to an ice climb called Silk Tassel, in Yoho National Park near Field, British Columbia. They separated into two teams of two and started up the near vertical ice, climbing parallel with each other.

That morning they had discussed the avalanche hazard. They planned to start early and finish the climb in an hour and be back down before the warmest part of the day. Their concern was the unseasonably warm daytime temperatures and sunny skies that were bringing spring-like avalanche conditions to the February snowpack. About 20 to 25 cm of snow had fallen on a surface hoar layer and with the above freezing temperatures this layer was sliding easily.

The climb they had chosen, though, faced due south and had been getting direct sun for 2 to 3 hours before they started climbing. Their plans of an early start turned into a noon-time start on the ice, by which time the air had warmed, reaching a maximum of 8°C. A couple of small sluffs had come down, but the climbers disregarded this and continued with their planned route.

At 12:30 the two lead climbers were about 5 m up the frozen waterfall, only about 3 m apart, side by side. The two belayers were at the bottom. Suddenly a much larger avalanche came down from above and poured heavy wet snow over the four climbers for at least a minute. During this deluge the climber on the right was plucked off the ice and carried 90 m down to the toe of the deposit. He ended up partially buried with only his legs, below the knees, sticking out. His belayer had been pulled out of a cave in which he was standing and was also partially buried. The climbers on the left had fared better. The one on the ice had hung on with his ice axes and his belayer has been only knocked aside briefly.

When the snow stopped pouring down on them, the belayer on the left quickly lowered her partner and they started searching for the other two. The partially buried belayer was quickly found and helped out. He had hurt his neck and was bleeding slightly but seemed otherwise all right. The rope was still connected between the two climbers and they followed it down to where the other person was buried. The snow was packed solid so they started digging him out using an ice axe. They had left their shovels in the car and as it was only possible for one person to dig at a time, one of the two unhurt climbers ran down to get the shovels as well as to call for help.

Down at the road he flagged down a passing car, which happened to have ambulance personnel in it. One of them grabbed a shovel as well and joined the climber going back up to the accident site. The other person in the car went for help.

*Fig. 6.7 Silk Tassel, 92-02-26. X - deceased.*

In the meantime, the rescuer was digging furiously and could hear a groan from the buried climber. She managed to get him out of the snow minutes later but by this time he had stopped breathing. Her hands were too cold from digging to feel a pulse and she decided to give him artificial respiration. At the same time the hurt belayer was stumbling around in shock; he was incoherent and did not respond to any suggestions from the rescuer. She, however, was too busy with the life threatening situation to help him. When her partner returned with help they moved the unconscious victim a couple of metres because the location was very awkward. They could not feel a pulse and initiated CPR. After 10 to 15 minutes without im-

provement they decided that they were in danger of further avalanches and moved everyone down another 10 m to a safer spot.

The park wardens arrived and took over the CPR. A helicopter then slung both victims out and they were transported to the Banff Hospital. The injured belayer had suffered a cervical fracture. The buried climber was pronounced dead on arrival.

**Source:** Terry Willis, Yoho National Park

**Comment:** Above 0°C temperatures and sunny skies can quickly increase the avalanche danger, especially on south-facing slopes. Careful consideration must be given to route selection in relation to weather and avalanche conditions, not just those below treeline but also conditions up high. Also, warning signs such as sluffing must be heeded. A decision to turn around may be the best option. It may save a life.

---

# Mt. Dagon, Monarch Icefields, Coast Mountains

22 April 1992

- **two climbers killed**
- **extensive search by co-operating government agencies**

| Weather Conditions at Bella Coola, 40 m above sea level, 65 km NW of accident site | | | | |
|---|---|---|---|---|
| Date 1992 | Max. Temp. (°C) | Min. Temp. (°C) | Precip. (mm) | Remarks |
| 04-16 | 17.8 | 7.5 | 4.8 | Overcast, showers |
| 04-17 | 13.2 | 8.2 | 2.0 | Clouds, showers and some wind all day |
| 04-18 | 16.1 | 7.3 | 0.0 | Scattered clouds, mostly sunny, cool wind |
| 04-19 | 15.2 | 3.9 | 4.8 | Cloudy with rain |
| 04-20 | 12.6 | 5.7 | 0.6 | Mostly cloudy |
| 04-21 | 11.8 | 3.0 | 2.2 | Cloudy with showers |
| 04-22 | 14.0 | 1.4 | 0.0 | Cloudy |

A couple left Bella Coola on April 17th for a 9-day ski tour on the Monarch Icefields, including climbing of nearby peaks. The 1000 km² Monarch Icefields dominate this remote area in the Coast Mountains, approximately 64 km southeast of Bella Coola, BC.

A search was initiated when the couple did not return as planned. From a journal recovered afterwards and from portions of their tracks observed much later, rescuers determined that the couple had ascended the Monarch Icefields as far as Mt. Erehwon and Mt. Dagon. Based on the unsettled weather in Bella Coola, most days of their trip up the icefields likely included snowfall and sometimes blowing snow. On April 21st they were tent-bound by a storm that de-

posited 60 cm of snow. The next day they attempted to climb Mt. Erehwon and Mt. Dagon. They probably reached the summit of Mt. Erehwon since their tracks were observed within 70 m of the peak. From Mt. Erehwon they toured northeast to the west face of Mt. Dagon, leaving their skis at the base of the mountain and continuing the ascent on foot. Rescuers suspect the couple was climbing over a convexity just above a snow-filled bergschrund and 100 m below the summit when an avalanche hit them and buried them together on the lower lip of the bergschrund (Fig. 6.8).

On April 27th they were reported overdue by a co-worker with whom they had left a trip plan and descriptions of their clothing and tent.

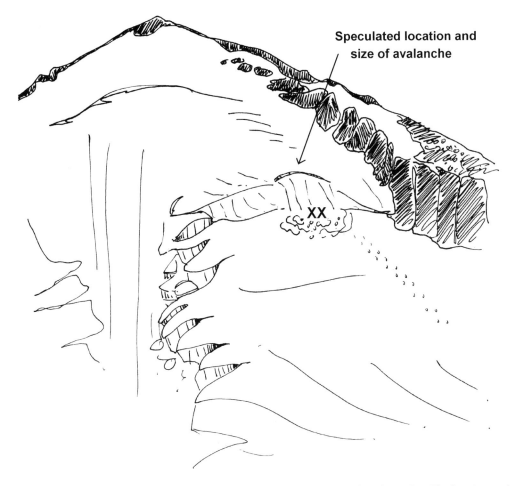

**Speculated location and size of avalanche**

XX

*Fig. 6.8  Mt. Dagon, 92-04-22. X - the bodies of the two climbers were found together. The location and size of the avalanche is speculative.*

This initiated one of the largest mountain search and rescue efforts in Canada. Searchers from British Columbia's Provincial Emergency Program (42 volunteers from 8 districts), the RCMP, the Justice Institute, Parks Canada as well as aircraft and personnel from the 442nd Squadron gathered in Bella Coola for the search.

Up to five helicopters were involved in the search of the Monarch Icefields. On April 30th a Labrador helicopter involved in the search crashed, killing one person and injuring nine. The search continued but stormy weather and heavy snowfalls made flying difficult. The passage of time progressively reduced the possibility of a live recovery. On May 6th, the search by government agencies was reduced to occa-sional overflights in hopes of spotting the tent or bodies after the heavy spring snowfalls had melted. A small private team continued to search the Monarch Icefields for the couple.

The tent was spotted from the air on July 18th and recovered along with the couple's journal the next day. The two bodies were spotted July 31st on Mt. Dagon and recovered the following day, 101 days after the couple was buried. Autopsies revealed they had asphyxiated.

**Source:** Ross Cloutier, Kamloops

**Comment:** The couple apparently continued the ascent up the icefields and onto the steep slope of Mt. Dagon in spite of recent snowfalls.

Although the poor weather frustrated the search effort, the trip plan left with a co-worker helped narrow down the search area.

During the combined ground and air search in late April and early May, attempts were made to locate signals from the couple's avalanche transceivers. To search crevasses, the searchers extended earphone cables to 15 m and lowered transceivers down crevasses to "listen" for transmitting units. Since no loss of signal strength was noticed with this technique, it may prove useful in future search and rescue efforts.

In recent years, personal locator-transmitters (PLT's) have become available for persons travelling in remote areas. The signals from PLT's are picked up by satellites and can be used to locate persons in difficulty just as signals from emergency locator-transmitters (ELT's) have been used to locate downed aircraft for many years. However, it is unlikely that such devices would help avalanche victims or avalanche rescue teams since the PLT's must be activated manually, and an avalanche leaves little time for such action.

---

# Snow Dome, Jasper National Park

20 March 1993

- **three climbers killed**
- **extreme terrain**

From the Icefields Parkway between Lake Louise and Jasper, a steep 750 m ice climb known as "Slipstream" is visible on the northeast face of Snow Dome. Three climbers were seen at the base of the route at 10:00 on March 20th and reported overdue the next day. Certainly, the wind had been depositing wind slabs on lee slopes such as Slipstream.

Due to stormy weather, wardens were unable to see the upper third of the route or the upper Athabasca Glacier for three days. Natural avalanches were observed in the Icefields during this period. On March 24th, wardens spotted fingers of a glove sticking through fresh snow on top of an avalanche deposit. This clue led to the recovery of one body. The other bodies were later found in a huge crevasse at the base of the route, one in June and one in August.

**Source:** Jasper Park Warden Service

**Comment:** In steep terrain, even relatively small avalanches can cause serious falls. Although extreme routes such as Slipstream always involve considerable risk, the climbers chose to ascend this route during a period of increasing avalanche danger.

# Hummingbird Ridge, Mount Logan, Yukon

24 May 1993

- **one mountaineer killed**
- **rock-fall triggered**

Three climbers left their advanced base camp at 03:00 on May 24th to attempt a new route on the south face of Mount Logan, in Yukon's Kluane National Park. They skied to the foot of a buttress and then started to climb up a steep snow couloir they had reconnoitred five days before. Climbing conditions were good and they were rapidly gaining elevation.

The past four days had seen warm but bad weather with periods of rain and snow. That morning, when they left their camp, the temperature had been -8°C and although still slightly overcast, the weather was steadily improving and the temperature was rising at about 2°C per hour.

At 04:15 they had reached a point about 100 m above where they had left their skis, when some huge boulders broke loose from an arete another 100 m above them. The boulders fell into the snow couloir and started a mixed snow and rock avalanche which swept all three climbers back down the face into a heavily crevassed area (Fig. 6.9).

*Fig. 6.9  Hummingbird Ridge, 93-05-24. 1 to 3 - location of climbers when avalanche started. X - deceased. S - survivors.*

Two of the climbers were only partially buried and they quickly freed themselves. The third climber, however, was completely buried and when the other two found him by using probes, he was already dead.

**Source:** Lloyd Freese, Kluane National Park

**Comment:** There will always be an inherent level of risk when venturing into the mountains. Being aware of the risks and accepting them is part of the experience.

---

# Mt. Temple, Banff National Park

9 August 1993

## • two climbers caught and one killed

At 07:00 on August 9th, two experienced climbers started up the Aemmer Couloir on Mt. Temple near Lake Louise, Alberta. They climbed quickly, passing several rock outcrops in the snow gully. As a result of unusually cool weather that summer, considerable snow remained on the upper levels of the mountains.

Rock outcrops in the gully forced them into a narrow channel that avalanches had scoured down the middle of the snow gully. Above the rock outcrops they stayed in the channel, increasing their risk. Half an hour after starting, they were already three quarters of the way up the 500 m-high gully when they were hit by a wet slide and carried to the base. Both were initially unconscious but regained consciousness. The woman had a broken femur and could not walk. The man had broken ribs and facial injuries. About an hour after the accident, he started to hike to get help. Because of his injuries, he hiked slowly, sitting down and passing out, sometimes every 50 m. After two days in cool weather with rain and snow, having travelled only 2 km over rough talus, he met a hiker near Lake Annette. The hiker relayed the message about the injured woman to the Lake Louise Visitor Centre mid-day on August 11th.

The climbers had been reported overdue about midnight on August 10th. Banff Park Wardens were searching by helicopter the next day when they were notified about the locations of the two climbers. They flew to the base of the couloir where they found that the woman had died. Due to the cold wet weather, hypothermia contributed to her death. Wardens picked up the man at Lake Annette and flew him to hospital in Banff.

**Source:** Banff Park Warden Service

**Comment:** Climbers often start ascents well before dawn, partly because summer avalanches and rockfall are more common during afternoon warming. However, this avalanche occurred around 07:30 in the morning when the sun first hit the gully walls above the climbers, suggesting that freezing levels had been high the night before. Normally an early start would ensure that climbers were above the snow gully before the snow was weakened by afternoon warming.

The avalanche was probably triggered by a cornice-like snow mushroom that fell off the side of the gully.

# Raven Lake, Cariboo Mountains

18 February 1995

- **two people killed**
- **storm snow on a crust**
- **subsequent avalanches**

There was a hard crust on the snow surface on February 17th and four hikers were able to walk up to the cabin at Raven Lake, some 100 km southeast of Prince George, British Columbia. They stayed there that night and woke up to 40 cm of new snow. It had warmed up rapidly. The temperature was above freezing and rain mixed with heavy snow was falling. There was also a strong wind. In the afternoon, three of them went to climb a nearby slope, intending to slide back down on garbage bags.

They were ascending a 30-35° slope near the mouths of some couloirs when an avalanche released around them (Fig. 6.10). When it stopped, about 100 m down-slope, one person found himself partially buried and was able to free himself. Looking around he saw a glove on the snow nearby, dug around it with his hands and uncovered the head of the second person who was about 30 cm below the surface, alive and coughing. However, he could not get him out because the deposit was very hard. He could not see any sign of the third person. By this time he was very cold and exhausted so he went back to the cabin to get help.

When the person at the cabin heard what had happened, he went out to look while the survivor remained behind. Unable to locate the accident site because of the continuing storm, he went back to the cabin for more directions from the survivor and then went out again to search. While climbing a slope which he thought was the location of the accident (but in fact was some distance away) he triggered another avalanche which buried him up to his neck. He was able to free himself. By this time it was almost dark with blizzard conditions so he abandoned the search and returned to the cabin to look after the survivor. They spent the night there.

The next morning the two remaining party members left the cabin and walked back to their truck which was parked on a logging road 5 km away. They were unable to move the truck because about 40 cm of new snow had fallen overnight. By this time the survivor was exhausted and hypothermic so he remained at the truck while the other person walked toward the highway 13 km away. Several kilometres from the highway he met a group of snowmobilers who used their radiophone to call the police. This was at about 16:00, 24 hours after the accident had occurred. The snowmobilers retrieved the survivor from the stalled truck and ambulances were dispatched to pick up the two and take them to hospital.

Prince George Search and Rescue were notified of the accident shortly after the police received the report and immediately began to mobilise a search party. Due to a mix-up in communication they were mistakenly under the impression that the accident had happened thirty minutes before. A helicopter left Prince George with a three-member search party aboard. As they arrived over the accident site at 15:40 they were notified that the accident had happened 24 hours ago. A quick aerial search was carried out, but because of the new snow and approaching darkness, evidence of the avalanche could not be seen and the helicopter returned to Prince George.

On the morning of February 20th the search leader, accompanied by the person who was caught in the second avalanche, arrived at the accident site by helicopter. Searchers, including a police officer and his dog from the Prince George detachment, were flown up to the site. Heavy wet snow covered the site and it was not possible to identify the deposit area.

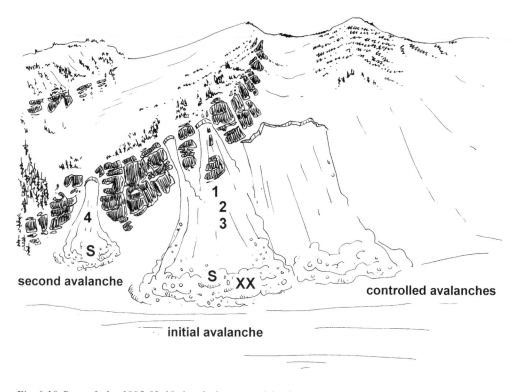

second avalanche

controlled avalanches

initial avalanche

*Fig. 6.10 Raven Lake, 1995-02-18. 1 to 3 - location of the three people when the initial avalanche started. 4 - location of searcher when second avalanche started. X - deceased. S - survivors.*

Going on information obtained from the witness, a search of the area by the dog was begun. Because the avalanche danger was considered *high* and the police officer and his dog did not have formal avalanche training, it was necessary to take extra precautions (e.g. the officer remained in a safe place while he directed the dog). Searching with the dog continued for several hours but was unsuccessful, so probe crews were organised.

Prior arrangements had been made to have explosives brought to the site to control the threatening slopes before probe crews began their search. The search leader, who was qualified in avalanche blasting, bombed the slope from a helicopter, releasing several size 2 slabs which ran onto the search area. Probe crews then began searching, and continued unsuccessfully until evening. The search was suspended until the next morning. The survivor of the fatal avalanche was released from hospital and

flown to the site in mid-afternoon and more information was obtained, but it was sketchy. Search crews spent the night at the cabin.

Early the next morning (February 21st), two avalanche-trained dog masters and their dogs arrived on site, one from the police detachment in Vernon, British Columbia and one from Parks Canada in Jasper, Alberta. They were briefed and began their search while the other searchers stood by for assistance. Three hours of searching with the dogs produced several indications but, when checked out, nothing was found. Probers continued checking the dogs' indications while others ran probe lines and carried out random probing. At about 14:00 a random prober struck a resilient object about 2 m down. The probe was dug out and the two victims' bodies were found in a horizontal position, one on top of the other.

The deposit of the controlled avalanches where the victims were found was 1 m deep. This and the fact that the victim who was par-

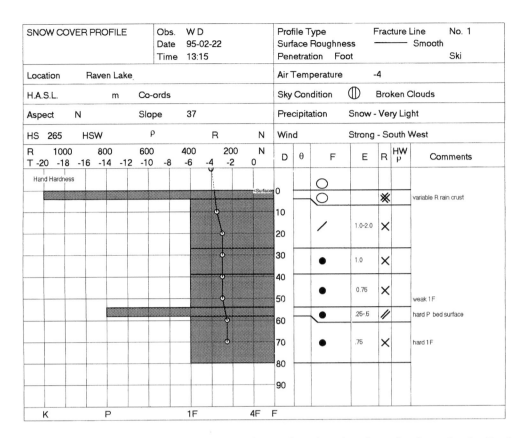

*Fig. 6.11 Fracture line profile for the Raven Lake accident, done four days after the avalanche. Total depth of snow was 265 cm. Shovel tests indicated very easy shears at 39 and 54 cm. The failure at 54 cm occurred while cutting the back of the second test. Surface hoar 2-3 mm and facets found at interface. Some surface hoar also found at 39 cm. Crown showed initial failure was at 39 cm but quickly stepped down to 54 cm.*

tially uncovered by the survivor was only 30 cm below the surface, and that the depth of the victims when found was over 2 m, indicates that there had been another avalanche over the first one.

Because of the large amount of new snow it was not possible to determine the sliding layer of the avalanche, the fracture line or its size. It is almost certain that it was a slab from the survivor's explanation of how it released. It is probable that the avalanche slid on a crust that was at the bottom of the layer which fell on the night of February 17th (Fig. 6.11).

**By:** George Evanoff

**Comment:** This case again shows how a total lack of awareness can lead to disaster.

The search and rescue operation which followed shows the various types of resources available. However, they usually become little more than body recovery operations when an avalanche burial is involved. The onus is on the accident party to rescue their own members.

# Cascade Mountain, Banff National Park

24 February 1995

- **two climbers killed**
- **warm, wet weather affecting winter snowpack**
- **route prone to avalanches**

| Date 1995 | Max. Temp. (°C) | Min. Temp. (°C) | Precip. (mm) |
|---|---|---|---|
| 02-24 | 6.5 | 1.0 | 0.4 |
| 02-25 | 4.5 | 1.0 | 0.0 |
| 02-26 | -8.0 | -12.5 | 0.0 |
| 02-27 | -6.5 | -22.0 | 0.0 |
| 02-28 | -7.5 | -23.0 | 0.0 |
| 03-01 | -2.0 | -25.0 | 0.0 |

Weather Conditions at Banff, Alberta
1385 m above sea level, 5 km SSW of accident site

An ice climber with one year of experience and a friend on his first snow and ice climb set out to ascend Bankhead Gully. This is a 300 m-high gully carved into the south face of Mt. Cascade near Banff, Alberta. Above the gully is a large bowl from which avalanches, even small ones, funnel down the gully (Fig. 6.12). February 24th was unusually warm; by noon it was drizzling.

The twosome probably reached the top of the ice climb. They were descending in a narrow, steep section by rappelling when struck by an avalanche. One had attached himself to a bolt fixed in the rock for rappelling and belaying, and was killed by the avalanche. The other was swept down the gully and buried.

Banff Park Wardens were notified that the party was missing at 20:42 in the evening. They went to the base of the gully and called up with a megaphone but heard no response. No lights were observed. Due to the continuing drizzle and resulting avalanche hazard, they decided against searching directly in the gully and continued the search the next morning when they could see into the gully from the safety of a helicopter.

At 07:20 on February 25th, they spotted the anchored climber near the top of the gully. They flew to a buttress on a rescue sling underneath

a helicopter and descended to the climber. After the climber's body was flown out, they and a search dog moved to a snow deposit further down the gully to search for the missing climber. After 30 minutes of searching without success, they were lifted out of the gully by helicopter because of the avalanche hazard.

On February 28th, after two days of much colder temperatures, they felt that the snow in and above the gully would be more stable and they flew to the top of the gully with a search dog. They descended the gully, searching for the second climber. Cold weather had frozen the snow so hard that their steel sectional probes could not penetrate it. Confident that the second climber was not alive, they suspended the search until the snow in the bowl above the gully was gone and the deposits in the gully had melted back.

In June, the gully was searched with dogs, again without success. At this time, the deposit was estimated to be 10 m deep. The second climber's body was spotted from the air on July 24th and flown out. The deposit had melted to an estimated depth of 5 m.

**Source:** Banff Park Warden Service

*Fig. 6.12 Bankhead gully on Cascade Mountain, 95-02-24. The photo shows the lower part of the large avalanche bowl above the route. Tim Auger photo.*

**Comment:** The climbers chose to climb the south-facing route on a warm winter day when rain was expected. Because of the avalanche hazard from the bowl above the gully, the recent guidebook for the area (Josephson, 1994, p. 111) states "don't even look at this route after the first snowfall of winter."

Rescuers limited their time in the gully during warm conditions because of the avalanche danger. On the 28th when they spent 3 hours descending the gully, the air temperature was much colder. Twenty hours later when the temperature was still cold, a size 3 avalanche roared down the gully, proving that natural avalanches occasionally start in cold conditions.

---

# Wedge Mountain, Whistler, BC

24 June 1995

- **one climber injured**
- **radio initiated rescue**

On June 24th, two climbers were descending the West Couloir of Wedge Mountain near Whistler, BC. At 13:50 a size 2 avalanche hit the climbers, sweeping them down the gully. One climber suffered multiple fractures including a broken femur.

His partner went to Wedge Lake where he used a VHF radio to call for help. The call was picked up by a taxi driver in Whistler who notified the RCMP. A team from Whistler Search and Rescue flew to the deposit and lifted the injured climber to hospital.

**Source:** BC Parks and *The Province*, 27 June 1995.

**Comment:** The radio call played an essential part in the rescue. "If it had been delayed by five hours, I think the injuries were serious enough that he might have expired." Radios and, increasingly, cell phones are being used to call for help, avoiding the often slow trip to the trailhead.

---

# Sunwapta Peak, Jasper National Park

18 August 1995

- **four roped climbers caught**

Sunwapta Peak is 4 km east of the Icefields Parkway between Lake Louise and Jasper.

On August 18th, a rope team of four climbers approached 3080 m on Sunwapta Peak in Jasper National Park. On a 35° slope just below a corniced ridge, the lead climber triggered a size 1.5 slab avalanche. All four were pulled down to the deposit, 30 m below the crown. Two were not buried and two were partly buried—one to the waist.

The 30 m-wide crown reached a maximum thickness of 40 cm and tapered to 5 cm at both sides. The wind slab was deposited on the northeast facing slope by recent winds.

**Source:** Jasper Park Warden Service

**Comment:** Although roped climbing can reduce the risk of certain mountaineering accidents, this minor incident illustrates that it can increase the avalanche hazard. In more serious avalanche terrain, the decision to "rope up" or not depends on which alternative presents the least risk for the group.

---

# Mt. Cerebrus, Monarch Icefields, near Bella Coola

17 May 1996

- **three climbers killed**
- **carried over cliff**
- **unseasonable snowpack**

As part of a three-week ski tour of the Monarch Icefield area, a party of five experienced ski tourers were on an ascent of the west face of Mt. Cerebrus following an approach via the east and south sides. Mt. Cerebrus (3140 m) borders the west side of the Monarch Icefield and is situated approximately 50 km southeast of Bella Coola, British Columbia, in the central Coast Mountains. One of the members decided to turn around at the base of the steep (35-45°) west face because she "did not like the steep slopes on the route" and skied back toward their camp.

Climbing 60 vertical metres further up the west face the group stopped and dug a pit to evaluate the snowpack stability. One of the survivors stated, *"Despite being May, the recent stormy, cold conditions had left significant storm snow and generally winter snow conditions. Three shovel tests and a rutschblock score of 4 indicated that the lower snowpack was quite solid - even at an obvious double ice crust 1 m down. However, there were moderate shear instabilities in the upper storm snow approximately 30 cm down. The decision was made after group deliberations that it was not advisable to continue on skis but that climbing a more vertical line of ascent on foot would be safe (less likely to shear the shallow unstable layer). We ascended the glacier diagonalling steady up to the right, unroped with ski poles. When it became obvious half-way up that the climb would require continuing further up to the right of the face we stopped again."* Here the survivor decided: *"...the risk was too high for my comfort zone so I descended and began building a windbreak for a group lunch shelter, as well as watching the progress of the other three."*

Early May was very cool with significant snowfall and unusually low freezing levels. The previous four days were unstable, stormy and cool. Daily new snow averaged 4-6 cm and temperatures were -3 to -10°C. On May 17th the weather was less adverse with increasing overcast through the morning and moderate temperatures from -3 to -5°C.

From his vantage point he saw the accident unfold. It was approximately 12:45. *"They reached the uppermost visible crevasse and were in the process of passing it when the slope released. From below it appeared that the storm snow instability released up high and triggered a bigger release lower on the slope (the ice layer 1 m down). The three climbers were likely swept off the cliff (200-300 m) over the icefall and down to the basin below."* The climbers were quite close to each other at the time the avalanche released (Fig. 6.13).

The party member that had turned back earlier was now returning to meet the others due to poor visibility on the ski route back to camp. The avalanche released as she continued up to meet the person building the windbreak on the flatter ground below the peak. *"I heard a bang and looked up to see an avalanche coming off*

*Fig. 6.13 Mount Cerebrus, 96-05-17. 1 to 3 - location of three climbers when avalanche started. X - deceased.*

*the cliffs of Cerebrus towards me. I immediately turned and tried to run away but was knocked over by the wind and spray. I was not buried and after the spray passed I continued up. I could see him getting out his shovel and could not see the others."*

All the group members wore avalanche transceivers so they immediately began to sweep the deposit, quickly finding poles and articles of clothing confirming that all three had been carried down. One of the survivors: *"Over approximately 20 minutes we located and partially dug out all three. None exhibited pulse, pupil response or any other sign of life."* The first victim was uncovered in about 1 minute, having been partially buried with part of his pack showing. The second recovery was about 5 minutes later and the last was within the 20 minutes. The two buried climbers were both buried under about 1 m of snow.

With small pieces of ice and snow still falling off the icefall and cliff, the two survivors became concerned for their own safety and quickly moved off to the side. They returned to the site in order to recover some rescue and crevasse gear from one of the victim's pack for their retreat. They left the bodies partially buried having determined there was nothing further they could do for their friends. One victim's transceiver was left on "transmit". The two survivors returned to their camp and prepared for the three-day ski out via Talchako, Hanlen Falls and Atnarko to their truck.

Search and rescue personnel from Whistler and Pemberton flew to the site by helicopter on May 23rd. After a stability evaluation, the bodies were located and recovered from under light amounts of new snow.

The avalanche was a size 2.5 dry slab which released on a 37° glaciated slope at 3100 m just above the uppermost crevasse on the west aspect of Mt. Cerebrus. Dimensions of the initial slab release in the storm snow were 30 cm deep by 60 m wide. This slab may have been unsupported because of the crevasse down-slope. The deeper slab 50 m down-slope was from 40 cm to 1.5 m deep and 90 m wide, stepping into the older snow layer, possibly along the climbers' steps. Significant ice blocks from the icefall were entrained in the debris, adding to the destructive potential of the mixed motion avalanche. The avalanche occurred close to the warmest time of day with the slope possibly receiving re-radiant warming through the cloud cover which was at summit level.

**By:** Scott Aitken, BC Ministry of Transportation and Highways

**Comment:** This accident involved two veteran skiers with up to 20 years of experience which included numerous five-week ski tours in the Yukon and Coast Mountains. The known consequences of their route selection may have been overpowered by the frustration of being tent bound previous to the break in the weather. Underestimating the unusually wintry spring snowpack might also have factored in the judgement of the victims.

The climbers took the rutschblock score of 4 as an indication of stability. However, 40-50% of slopes with rutschblock scores of 4 can be skier triggered (Föhn, 1987; Jamieson and Johnston, 1995b).

Fracture line data were unobtainable because of increasing instability due to solar radiation on the west face at the time of the body recovery. Loose wet avalanches overran the upper burial site one and a half hours after the rescue team cleared the area.

# Mount Logan, Kluane National Park

5 June 1996

- **one climber killed**
- **no transceivers**

On June 5th, a group of four climbers was tackling the east ridge of Mount Logan in Kluane National Park, in the Yukon. They were at 4100 m, heading up a 35° snow slope through a serac field, following a flagged route left by a previous party. One of the climbers was out front, kicking steps into the fresh snow that had recently fallen. He was a few hundred metres ahead of the rest of the group when they saw an avalanche start and carry him back down the slope towards them. The size 2 avalanche was about 20 m wide and stopped running after about 200 m. However, it had carried him over a 15 m ice cliff and completely buried him under 1 m of snow.

The other three climbers searched the deposit by probing with their ice axes and digging in likely spots. They were not wearing avalanche transceivers. After about 45 minutes they located the body and started CPR but he did not respond. He also appeared to have a broken neck, which he probably sustained in his fall over the ice cliff. At that elevation the body was unrecoverable, so they left it behind in a crevasse.

**Source:** Rick Staley, Kluane National Park

**Comment:** Mountaineers are often as prone to avalanche danger as skiers and snowmobilers. Carrying the proper avalanche rescue equipment is just as necessary.

# Chapter 7

# Residential, Industrial and Transportation Accidents

## Kildala Pass, Coast Mountains

17 February 1985

- **Power line damaged**

The high voltage transmission line between the generating station at Kemano and the aluminum smelter at Kitimat, British Columbia crosses Kildala Pass (elevation 1510 m). The line is in the Coast Mountains where the snowfall is heavy. For a distance of 15 km over the pass, the transmission line is split into two single, parallel circuits. The line on the right side (identified by R) is carried on steel lattice towers, and the line on the left (L) is on towers that were built with aluminum tubing.

On February 17$^{th}$ an avalanche on the north side of Kildala Pass destroyed tower 124L and caused minor damage to steel members of the adjacent towers 123R and 124R at an elevation of 740 m. The single circuit R was able to maintain the delivery of power.

Weather observations at Kitimat led to the conclusion that about 200 mm of precipitation had fallen on the five days prior to the avalanche occurrence. This precipitation and previous snow falls probably created an approximately 190 cm-deep unstable snowpack in the avalanche path.

The avalanche starting zone, at 1700 m, was on a northeast facing slope with a 39° incline and lee to the prevailing storm wind. After running down an open 31° slope, the avalanche

was deflected by a 50 m-high ridge. It then moved over 400 m on gentle incline between 0° and 10° along the opposite valley side, towards the power line. Models of avalanche dynamics and the runout distance of the avalanche led to the conclusion that the avalanche speed at the tower 124L was approximately 24 m/s. The avalanche snow was dry and probably had a deep powder component. The age of broken trees in the avalanche path suggested that an avalanche of similar magnitude had not occurred for close to 100 years. The mode of failure of the tower, which had five legs of aluminum tube supporting a cross arm, could not be established exactly. The combination of impact pressure from dense avalanche snow at the legs plus pressures and oscillations of the powder snow at the conductors, cross arm and upper parts of the legs, probably caused a progressive failure of individual structural elements. Pieces of the broken tower were carried away in the avalanche. In the weeks following the accident, tower 124L was re-built with stronger bracing of the legs.

**By:** Peter Schaerer

**Comment:** The transmission line between Kemano and Kitimat has a history of destructive avalanches. The line was completed in 1954 and already by January 26th 1955, avalanches had destroyed three towers in Glacier Bowl at the south side of Kildala Pass, interrupting both single circuits and the delivery of power to Kemano. In the summer of 1955, a unique protection was built by suspending the conductors in Glacier Bowl on 1180 m-long wire ropes spanning transversely across the bowl. The suspension eliminated towers on the ground in Glacier Bowl and kept the power conductors out of harm.

Earth and steel deflectors were built at other exposed towers in following years. On January 22nd 1973, an avalanche destroyed tower 105L. Subsequently, the legs of tower 105L and tower 105R were protected by placing strong steel breakers in front of them. On December 27th 1992, tower 113R near the summit of Kildala Pass was damaged (see Kildala Pass - 27 December 1992 write-up in this publication).

---

# Mt. Stephen, near Field, BC

12 February 1986

- **size 4 avalanche**
- **semi-trailer truck hit while driving**
- **avalanche across Trans Canada Highway**

It was just after 01:00 when a trucker was driving his rig along the Trans Canada Highway near Field, British Columbia. Far above him, a size 4 avalanche had just let go from Mt. Stephen. It had started near the top of the mountain near the face of the glacier, and was plummeting 1500 m down the mountainside.

In the darkness the trucker could not see it coming and the large avalanche broadsided his semi-trailer truck, pushing him off the side of the road. The avalanche covered the highway, blocking any further traffic, and partially bur-

ied his truck. He sustained some minor injuries but was able to get out of his truck and climb back up the embankment to the highway. "It was bad but I've been beat up worse in a bar...".

Meanwhile, an employee of the Canadian Pacific Railway, which was also blocked, had reported the avalanche. Personnel from Yoho National Park responded to the scene. They helped the trucker to an ambulance and then questioned him as to whether there had been any other cars caught in the slide; he did not

think so. Just to be sure, avalanche dogs were brought to the scene to search the slide debris below the highway.

Road closures were put up at Lake Louise, Castle Junction and Golden. By 07:00, one lane was pushed through the avalanche debris and by 13:00 the Trans Canada Highway was once again in full operation. The overturned truck was removed and the Canadian Pacific Railway was reopened at about the same time.

**Source:** Terry Willis, Yoho National Park

**Comment:** Subsequent investigation indicated that the avalanche was either triggered by an ice fall or released and triggered an ice fall from the glacier – large amounts of glacier ice were found in the deposit. The avalanche had cleaned out the avalanche path so the hazard to the highway was minimal.

Remedial actions involved creating diversion channels and dams above the railway and highway as well as establishing an explosives stabilisation program.

This problem is primarily related to the calving of ice from the glacier – impossible to forecast and difficult to stabilise. Large dry avalanches will likely jump the diversion structures and continue to be a problem for the highway.

# Telegraph Creek, Coast Mountains, BC

28 January 1989

- **one person in house killed**

*Fig. 7.1 Telegraph Creek, 89-01-28. Eastern part of town after avalanche. The photo shows an intact house pushed off its foundation. Jack Bennetto photo.*

Telegraph Creek is a small Tahltan community on the Stikine River, 60 km southwest of Dease Lake. Motorised boats travel the river from Wrangell, Alaska and the Pacific Ocean to Telegraph Creek. By road it is 50 km southwest of Dease Lake. At only 185 m above sea level, the town usually receives more rain than snow in the winter.

A heavy storm hit Northern BC on the night of January 24th. One site reported 61 cm of snow in one 12-hour period, followed by 140 mm of rain. In low lying areas such as Telegraph Creek, a mixture of rain and snow fell. As the storm continued, the temperature in the town only fell to +1°C on the night of January 27th and rose to +3°C on the 28th. The rain and snow fell on a weak base of faceted crystals.

By January 28th most people in the east part of town had left their houses, fearing avalanches from the slope directly above. At noon a man warned his 80-year-old aunt, but she declined to leave her house. Two hours later, two back-to-back avalanches swept down the slope, removing most of the snow and hitting four houses. The occupied house was demolished. Much of it was pushed 30 m off its foundation and to the edge of the Stikine River. Two other houses were pushed off their foundations, and the remaining house was partly buried (Figs. 7.2 and 7.3).

A small amount of the avalanche deposit had entered the remains of the occupied house. The woman was found badly injured in her chair. Neighbours carried her to their house where she died.

**Source:** BC Ministry of Transportation and Highways and *The Province*, 28 January 1989

**Comment:** Avalanches from the same storm closed Highway 37 from Terrace to Dease Lake, Highway 37A to Stewart, Highway 16 from Terrace to Prince Rupert and the railway from Terrace to Prince Rupert. The avalanche at Ningunsaw Pass broke mature forest, depositing up to 15 m of snow and trees on Highway 37.

*Figure 7.2 Telegraph Creek, 89-01-28. The woman was fatally injured in this house. Jack Bennetto photo.*

*Figure 7.3 Telegraph Creek, 89-01-28. House damaged by the avalanche. Jack Bennetto photo.*

## Smith-Dorrien Highway, Kananaskis Country

1 February 1991

- **stopped automobile hit by avalanche**
- **warning sign disregarded**

On the evening of the 1ˢᵗ three friends drove their Bronco up the road leading from the Canmore Nordic Centre towards Spray Lakes in Alberta's Kananaskis Country. They had just passed a sign saying "Avalanche Area, No Stopping". However, they disregarded it and stopped their truck along the side of the road. They got out to enjoy the view and *"answer a call of nature"*.

The weather was unusually warm. This, combined with an already unstable snowpack, caused the avalanche hazard in Kananaskis Country to be high to extreme.

As they were getting back into the truck one of them spotted an avalanche coming down towards them in the moonlight. Not having enough time to start the truck and drive away, they started sprinting down the road. They could feel the spray from the avalanche at their backs but they had outrun the main snow component. Their truck was not so lucky. It was swept over the side of the road and carried about 35 m downhill. The guard rail along the road was also destroyed (Figs. 7.4 and 7.5).

They walked back down to town, relieved to be alive.

**Source:** George Field, Kananaskis Country

**Comment:** Avalanche warning signs are there for the public's safety and must be respected.

*Fig. 7.4 Smith-Dorrien Highway, 91-02-01. Avalanche over road and location of truck. George Field photo.*

*Fig. 7.5 Smith-Dorrien Highway, 91-02-01. Avalanche warning sign and deposit over road. George Field photo.*

# Kootenay Pass, Salmo-Creston Highway

22 December 1992

## • one moving vehicle hit by avalanche

| | | | | | | | | |
|---|---|---|---|---|---|---|---|---|
| Weather Conditions at Kootenay Pass Study Plot Elevation 1775 m | | | | | | | | |
| Date 1992 | Time | Sky/ Precip. | Max. Temp. (°C) | Min. Temp. (°C) | Snowfall (cm) | Storm Snow (cm) | Wind | |
| 12-20 | 05:55 | Obs S-1 | -9.0 | -12.0 | 12 | 18 | M - SW | |
| 12-20 | 14:55 | Obs S-1 | -8.0 | -9.0 | 5 | 23 | L - NW | |
| 12-21 | 06:25 | Obs S-1 | -8.0 | -9.0 | 12 | 34 | L - S | |
| 12-21 | 15:00 | Obs S-1 | -6.5 | -8.0 | 10 | 43 | L - S | |
| 12-22 | 06:00 | Obs S 3 | -6.5 | -8.0 | 8 | 47 | S - SE | |
| 12-22 | 15:40 | Obs S 2 | -4.5 | -7.5 | 15 | 57 | M - S | |

Most active avalanche control programs use explosives to release unstable snow from avalanche start zones, after restricting access to the avalanche path below. In the case of highways, the road is closed during explosive control and while snow plows remove any snow deposited on the highway by the controlled avalanches.

Avalaunchers are one device for delivering explosive charges into avalanche start zones. These canons use pressurised nitrogen to propel explosive projectiles, typically containing 1 kg of explosive, into avalanche start zones. Compared to military artillery such as recoilless rifles, avalaunchers are less expensive to operate but the relatively low speed of the projectiles allows their flight to drift in windy conditions. The storm conditions that often require avalanche control are sometimes accompanied by wind, fog and/or heavy snowfall. The wind can cause some projectiles to miss their target, and the fog or heavy snowfall makes it difficult for control crews to determine how much unstable snow has been removed from each start zone.

In December 1992, the avalanche control program at Kootenay Pass relied heavily on avalaunchers for avalanche control. A storm that started on December 18th caused several closures of the highway for avalanche control. On the morning of the 22nd, the highway was closed while the control team used the avalaunchers on Towers 1, 2, 3 and 5 to control avalanche paths above the highway. Shots from Tower 2 caused four avalanches to deposit 2-4 m of snow on the highway. The smallest of these deposits was from an avalanche path called "21.5". Halfway down this and neighbouring paths, a bench had been cut in the side of the mountain to prevent smaller slides from hitting the highway. However, during the avalanche control from Tower 2, large avalanches filled the bench with snow, reducing its effect on any subsequent slides.

The highway was open for most of the afternoon. It was open at 18:30 when a natural avalanche from path "21.5" hit a westbound car broadside. The car was pushed to the edge of the road, 300 m above the bottom of a creek. The avalanche dented the right side of the car and broke windows, causing minor cuts to the passenger's face. A highway maintenance foreman, who was on his way to start the night shift, was in one of the first vehicles to arrive. He quickly ensured that the car and occupants were removed from the deposit, in case other slides reached the highway. The highway was closed.

Analysis of events leading up to the accident suggest that not all of the unstable snow for path "21.5" had released during avalanche

control in the morning, and that 40-50 km/h winds from the southwest had re-loaded the start zone.

**Source:** John Tweedy, Kootenay Pass Avalanche Technician, BC Ministry of Transportation and Highways

**Comment:** Since this accident the avalaunchers have been replaced with recoilless rifles and three propane exploders positioned in start zones. Rounds from the recoilless rifles have a muzzle velocity of 400 m/s and spin in flight; consequently their trajectory is essentially unaffected by wind. The benches have also been enlarged.

In Canada, accidents such as this are very rare. Incidents in which people drive into recent avalanche deposits are more common, occurring about 10 times per year in BC.

---

# Kildala Pass, Coast Mountains

27 December 1992

- **power line tower hit**

On the 27th of December the Kemano-Kitimat power line in the Coast Mountains of British Columbia was hit by an avalanche near its highest point along the route.

A cold, clear period prior to the 18th of December had produced a weak layer of facets up to 4 cm thick sitting on 50 cm of multi-layered ice crusts. Between the 18th and 26th of December up to 250 cm of storm snow accumulated on top of the weak layer and formed into a stiff slab of pencil hardness. On the 27th, an Arctic front moved in and dropped the temperature to -22°C. Along with the cold, a strong northeast wind came up, transporting even more snow onto the unstable snowpack. This was probably the straw that broke the camel's back and the hard, storm-snow slab fractured 1000 m wide. Both the west and east aspects of Glacier Creek Bowl avalanched and ran about 1000 m down the 40° incline, not stopping until they reached 10° terrain. The avalanches were size 3 and 4 respectively.

One tower was totally destroyed, downing about 1 km of power line. Due to the inhospitable weather and terrain it took 43 days to reconstruct the tower and restore power to the line. Fortunately a parallel line was undamaged and was able to provide power for the interim. The parallel power line provides a backup power supply when various natural hazards destroy towers (e.g. rivers, rock slides, wind/rime). Nevertheless, the cost of repairing the damage came to over $1 million.

**Source:** Scott Flavelle

**Comment:** The power line was built in the early fifties and since then seven towers have been destroyed by avalanches, in five incidents. Three towers were destroyed in 1955 and then one each in 1957, 1973, 1985 and 1992. Some of the towers have now been reinforced and earth deflectors built above them.

# Kildala Pass, Coast Mountains

12 February 1994

- **six people trapped in emergency shelter**
- **exposed location**

On February 10th, two crews of six were flown by helicopter to Kildala Pass to restore a power line tower. Situated in the Coast Mountains of British Columbia between Kemano and Kitimat, at 1675 m, this is the highest point on the power line route. A small emergency shelter sat at the base of the damaged tower. As the first crew left with the helicopter, the weather deteriorated and the six people that were left knew they would have to stay there at least one night. The shelter is exposed to avalanches from Glacier Creek Bowl.

What follows are excerpts from a report written by one of the six people.

*"February 11.*

*Estimated 100 cm new snow by 12:00, light to moderate west wind, barometric pressure dropping steadily. 828 mb. Poor visibility.*

*...The entire day was spent shoring up the shack with double 2 x 12 pillars...preparing to stay there for an indefinite period.*

*With conditions still deteriorating everyone felt that this was a very dangerous place to be...and that the plywood shack was completely inadequate protection from a large avalanche. After a discussion in the evening a unanimous decision was made to move to the relative safety of Camp 11 the next morning...It would expose everyone to some avalanche danger until we reached the bluffs above the cat road.*

*We all tried to settle that night for what was to be a largely sleepless one with a high level of anxiety and tension building. There was a feeling of inevitability about our situation. Suddenly there was a deafening roar mixed with the noise of splintering wood. In an instant we were all up, petrified to the floor with shear terror...An avalanche had come from above*

*and hit the shack. The feeling of being exposed and extremely vulnerable was now a reality and palpable in those first few moments after 3 am.*

*A wave of relief spread through us when we realised that everyone was alright and that in spite of splintering joists the roof had held the snow load. How much debris was on top? How easily could we dig ourselves out? Was there still more avalanche danger? For how long would we have enough air under the snow? These thoughts were going through our minds as we began probing and digging out. It took only a few minutes to tunnel through 2 metres of snow...It was an immense relief to be outside and know we were not entombed in densely packed snow.*

*February 12.*

*Estimated 50-75 cm new snow, moderate SW winds, pressure bottomed out at 828 mb. Poor visibility.*

*We shovelled until 07:00, in shifts, clearing the average 2 m of snow from the roof...the roof was patched and benches were sawn into pillars and braces to reinforce the damaged areas.*

*...Another large avalanche shook the shelter at 10 am spilling us out of sleeping bags and had us rooted to the spot waiting for annihilation. The two outside shovelling were miraculously safe and had not heard or felt anything. The snow/air turbulence that we heard and felt inside (and by now deep down in the new snowpack and debris) indicated a fairly major avalanche had passed by...*

*Our plan to move to Camp 11 was reviewed and now rejected...the avalanche hazard was clearly extreme...The rest of the day passed without event.*

*February 13.*

*Estimated 20-30 cm new snow, light SW wind, pressure still low at 827 mb and zero visibility.*

*More shovelling, radio contact, no slides and favourable winds that were reducing the loading on the upper slopes around us...tramp out and mark a landing area...*

*The helicopter was in the air in the afternoon when we called to advise of improving conditions and reasonable visibility...All six were on the pad ready to leave...open area soon closed and visibility was too poor to fly...another hole opened up...quickly loaded and descended to Kemano all very relieved that we had been rescued and that this ordeal was over.*

*During the last few moments at the helipad we observed the remains of a fracture line between the towers on the pass. It was an estimated 2 m deep..."*

**Source:** Hector MacKenzie

**Comment:** Because of this incident, the shelter at Camp 12 is no longer used for overnight stays in the winter. All work is done with a helicopter on hand and in fair weather.

# Blanc-Sablon, Quebec

10 March 1995

- **two fatalities**
- **house destroyed**

On the evening of the 9th the residents of Goodchild Street went to sleep with an unusually intense blizzard blowing outside. Their little village of Blanc-Sablon lies between the 90 m escarpment of Mont Bonenfant and the Atlantic Ocean. It is situated in eastern Quebec, near the border with Labrador. Goodchild Street runs along the base of the escarpment.

The blizzard had been raging since the morning of the 8th and had dumped 82 cm during only the past 24 hours. In addition, the winds were gusting over 100 km/h, creating spectacularly deep drifts. One such drift built up along the top edge of the escarpment, accumulating more and more snow as the blizzard continued.

At just after two o'clock in the morning the drift became overloaded and broke free from the hillside. The resulting avalanche swept down the escarpment and hit one of the houses on Goodchild Street. It tore off the roof and pushed it onto the other side of the street. The snow then poured into the house burying a man, a woman and their son (Fig. 7.6).

At about 02:30 a neighbour happened to look out his window and saw the destruction. He raised the alarm and along with other residents of the village started digging in the debris. Even above the howling blizzard they were able to hear the screams of the buried woman. The digging was difficult due to the storm but they kept going in the direction of the call for help. It was not until about six hours after the avalanche had occurred that they were able to free her from under 3 m of snow. She was in shock and had frost-bitten feet. The diggers continued and shortly after also uncovered the bodies of her husband and son.

Due to the continued danger of avalanches from the escarpment, some 50 other residents of Goodchild Street were evacuated to the village's school. In the following days, army demo-

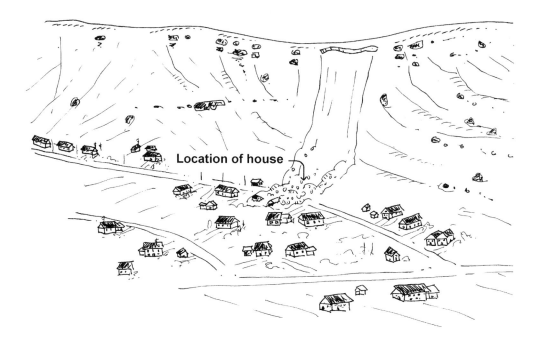

**Location of house**

*Fig. 7.6 Blanc-Sablon, 95-03-10. The two fatalities were inside the house buried by the avalanche. The house's roof was pushed across the road.*

lition experts used explosives to break up the huge drift but it proved a difficult task and it would be almost two weeks before the residents of Goodchild Street could return home.

In addition to the house, two sheds were destroyed, a power line was damaged and a pick-up truck was partially buried. In total the estimated cost of lost property came to $80 000.

**Source:** Marc Lavallée, Quebec Ministry of Public Safety

**Comment:** Avalanche accidents in residential or industrial areas have become increasingly rare throughout this century. Better land use plan-

ning through awareness of potentially dangerous areas has played the major role. In Europe and Iceland this is more of a problem with long established houses or villages located in avalanche run-out zones. There, various protective measures are taken to help safeguard the houses and their inhabitants.

In response to the above avalanche, a 3 m high by 1 km long snow fence was erected along the top of the cliff above Blanc-Sablon. This will reduce the build-up of drifts and decrease the risk of a similar tragedy.

# Conrad Kain Hut, Bugaboo Provincial Park

16 January 1996

- **exposed location**
- **heavy snowfall winter**

The Conrad Kain Hut is situated in Bugaboo Provincial Park, British Columbia and services climbers in the area during all but the winter months.

On January 16th a size 3 avalanche came off the snow field on Snowpatch Spire with a fracture line 1 to 1.5 m deep. The avalanche dropped about 350 m onto the moraines of Crescent Glacier and initiated a size 3.5 avalanche. The snowpack at this time of year was at a near-record high and reduced the influence of the rough terrain usually evident in the area. These two factors (deep snowpack and large avalanche) contributed to the avalanche reaching the hut. A large rock uphill from the hut acted as a wedge, splitting the avalanche into two parts, with the larger left arm giving the hut a glancing blow (Fig. 7.7).

Due to the deep snowpack the ground floor of the hut was protected and only the second floor was damaged. The back wall of the park ranger's room was demolished and part of the roof was pushed in. Damage was estimated at $25 000.

**Source:** Roger Tierney, BC Parks, East Kootenay District

**Comment:** Conrad Kain Hut has a history of being hit by avalanches. The location of the hut protects it against all but the largest avalanches; therefore, the only recommendation was to strengthen and winterise the back wall as a remedial action.

Fig. 7.7 Conrad Kain Hut, 96-01-16.

# References

CAA. 1995. Observation Guidelines and Recording Standards for Weather, Snowpack and Avalanches. Canadian Avalanche Association. P.O. Box 2759, Revelstoke, BC, Canada, 98 p.

Colbeck, S, E. Akitaya, R. Armstrong, H. Gubler, J. Lafeuille, K. Lied, D. McClung, and E. Morris. 1990. International Classification for Seasonal Snow on the Ground. International Commission for Snow and Ice (IAHS), World Data Center A for Glaciology, University of Colorado, Boulder, CO, USA, 23 p.

Föhn, P.M.B. 1987. The rutschblock as a practical tool for slope stability evaluation. Avalanche Formation, Movement and Effects, IASH Publ. 162 (Symposium at Davos 1986), 223-228.

Fredston, J., D. Fesler and B. Tremper. 1995. The human factor - lessons for avalanche education. Proceedings of the International Snow Science Workshop at Snowbird, International Snow Science Workshop 1994, P.O. Box 49, Snowbird, Utah 84092, USA, 473-486.

Gray, J.M.N.T., L.W. Morland and S.C. Colbeck. 1995. The effect of change in the thermal properties on the propagation of a periodic thermal wave: Application to a snow buried rocky outcrop. Journal of Geophysical Research, 100(B8) 15,267-15,279.

Jamieson, J.B. 1995. Avalanche prediction for persistent snow slabs. PhD Thesis, Dept. of Civil Engineering, University of Calgary, 258 p.

Jamieson, J.B. and C.D. Johnston. 1992. Snowpack characteristics associated with avalanche accidents. Canadian Geotechnical Journal 29, 862-866.

Jamieson, J.B. and C.D. Johnston. 1995a. Monitoring a shear frame stability index and skier-triggered slab avalanches involving persistent snowpack weaknesses. Proceedings of the International Snow Science Workshop at Snowbird, International Snow Science Workshop 1994, P.O. Box 49, Snowbird, Utah 84092, USA, 14-21.

Jamieson, J.B. and C.D. Johnston. 1995b. Interpreting rutschblocks in avalanche start zones. Avalanche News, 46, 2-4.

Josephson, J. 1994. Waterfall Ice - Climbs in the Canadian Rockies, third edition. Rocky Mountain Books, Calgary, 272 p.

LaChapelle, E.R. 1969. Field Guide to Snow Crystals. University of Washington Press, Seattle, 101 p.

Liverman, D. 1996. Letters to Canadian Geographic, Sept./Oct. 1996, p. 7.

Logan, N. 1993. Snow temperature patterns and artificial avalanche release. Proceedings of the International Snow Science Workshop in Breckenridge, Colorado, (Oct. 1992), 37-46.

McClung, D.M. and P.A. Schaerer. 1993. The Avalanche Handbook. The Mountaineers, Seattle, 271 p.

Morrall, J.F. and W.M. Abdelwahab. 1992. Estimating traffic delays and the economic cost of recurrent road closures on rural highways. Logistics and Transportation Review 29(2), 159-177.

Schaerer, P.A. 1987. Avalanche Accidents in Canada III. A Selection of Case Histories, 1978-1984, National Research Council of Canada, Institute for Research in Construction, Paper No. 1468, NRCC publication 27950, 138 p.

Schaerer, P.A. 1993. International Committee for Alpine Rescue: Meeting of the avalanche committee. Avalanche News 41, 4-6.

Stethem, C.J and P.A. Schaerer. 1979. Avalanche Accidents in Canada I. A Selection of Case Histories of Accidents, 1955 to 1976. National Research Council of Canada, Division of Building Research Paper 834, NRCC Publication 17292, 114 p.

Stethem C.J. and P.A. Schaerer. 1980. Avalanche Accidents in Canada II. A Selection of Case Histories of Accidents, 1943 to 1978. National Research Council of Canada, Division of Building Research Paper 926, NRCC Publication 18525, 75 p.

# Appendix A

# Reporting Avalanche Involvements

## Objective

The objective of reporting avalanche accidents and damage is to collect data about the extent of avalanche problems in Canada. Summaries of the reports will draw attention to avalanche dangers and assist in the development of safety measures.

## Reporting Forms

Two different reporting forms are available for recording avalanche accidents and damage.

The concise form is designed for reporting the fact that people or objects had an encounter with avalanches. This short report should be submitted every time people are involved in an avalanche or property is damaged. A blank avalanche involvement reporting form is included in this appendix.

The detailed reporting form allows the characteristics of the avalanche and details about the event to be recorded. The detailed report should be completed primarily for the records of the operation concerned, either when an avalanche caused a fatality, serious injury, or property damage in excess of $10 000 or when the incident has a high educational value. It may

be useful as a check list when operations may wish to describe an accident and the rescue work in greater detail. Blank forms are available from the Canadian Avalanche Centre.

## Filing of Reports

Completed concise reports should be returned as quickly as possible to the Canadian Avalanche Centre in Revelstoke.

The individual reports will be treated confidentially and the results will be made public in summary form only. Interesting cases will be included in publications of avalanche accident case histories, if the concerned reporters and involved persons and companies agree. The names of the reporters or victims are not required.

## Completion of the Short Form

## 1. Date and Time

Fill in the date and time of the avalanche occurrence.

## 2. Location

Give the name of the mountain area, high-way, or ski area and either a description, name, or number of the avalanche path.

## 3. Avalanche Description

Fill out the appropriate fields to the best of your knowledge.

## 4. Number of People

Enter the total number of people in the party and how many of them were either caught, partially buried or completely buried in the avalanche. Indicate how many people were injured or killed.

Under this section enter the number of people in buildings or vehicles buried or damaged by the avalanche.

*Note: The number of injured and dead people must be included in the numbers caught, partially buried and buried:*

*A person is <u>caught only</u> if he is touched by the avalanche but not covered with snow when the avalanche stops.*

*A person is <u>partially buried</u> if any part of the body is visible on the surface when the avalanche stops. People in vehicles which are partially buried must be reported here.*

*A person is <u>completely buried</u> if he is completely beneath the snow surface when the avalanche stops. Equipment such as skis or poles may be visible on the surface. People in vehicles which are buried must be reported here.*

## 5. Activity of People

Write the type of activity being done by the people at the time of the avalanche for those that were caught or partially or completely buried; e.g. skiing, mountain climbing, avalanche control, travel on the road, snow plowing.

## 6. Number of Vehicles

Indicate the number of vehicles that were either trapped, partially buried or buried. Indicate how many of them were damaged.

*Note: Vehicles include those on roads, rails, as well as over-snow vehicles and aircraft.*

*A vehicle is <u>trapped</u> if it is blocked by avalanche deposits in front of and behind it, or if it became stuck when it tried to cross or ran into an avalanche deposit.*

*A vehicle is <u>partially buried</u> if any part is still visible when the avalanche stops.*

*A vehicle is <u>buried</u> if it is completely beneath the snow surface when the avalanche stops.*

## 7. Structures Damaged

Enter the number and type of structural damages. For example, include the function and construction type of buildings, the number of poles and length of telephone line or power line, the type of lift towers, a bridge, etc. Estimate the loss in dollar terms whenever possible.

## 8. Estimated Depth of Burial

For buried people and vehicles, give the depth between the highest part of the body or vehicle and the avalanche surface.

## 9. Estimated Duration of Burial

Estimate the time between the occurrence of the avalanche and when the person or object was uncovered.

## 10. Comments

Make brief notes on the principal cause of the avalanche encounter. Examples include the weather (snowfall, wind, temperature), snow conditions, skiers entering a closed area and triggering the avalanche.

Add any comments that might be significant; for example whether or not warnings of high snow instability were available, search by transceiver, type of injury, etc; otherwise refer to the detailed report.

# Avalanche Involvement Report

**CANADIAN AVALANCHE ASSOCIATION**

**(Concise form)**

**DATE** (year, month, day)_____

**TIME** (hour, min)        ____ : ___  ( 24 hr clock)

**LOCATION** _____

## AVALANCHE DESCRIPTION

Size (1.0 to 5.0)   __.__          Elevation _____
Aspect _____          Incline _____
Type (check one) Loose __ Slab __          Slab Width ____          Thickness ___.__
Liquid Water in Deposit (check one) Dry __    Moist __    Wet __
Trigger _____
Sliding Layer (If known) _____

| **PEOPLE** | Number of People | Number of People Wearing Transceivers | | |
|---|---|---|---|---|
| | | 457 kHz | 2.275 kHz | Dual |
| Total in party | _____ | _____ | _____ | _____ |
| Caught only | _____ | _____ | _____ | _____ |
| Partially buried | _____ | _____ | _____ | _____ |
| Completely buried | _____ | _____ | _____ | _____ |
| Injured | _____ | _____ | _____ | _____ |
| Fatalities | _____ | _____ | _____ | _____ |

**ACTIVITY OF PEOPLE** _____
_____

**EQUIPMENT LOST** _____
**VEHICLES** (number)

Trapped _____          Partially Buried _____
Completely Buried _____          Damaged _____
Type of Vehicles _____
**STRUCTURES DAMAGED** _____
_____

Estimated total property loss          $____ , _____ , _____.00

Estimated Depth of Burial (m)          ____ . __     ____.__     ____.__
Estimated Duration of Burial (hrs, min)    ____ : ___    ____ : ___    ____ : ___
**COMMENTS** (Snowpack, Burial, Search and Rescue details, please attach additional pages if necessary.): _____
_____

Name and Address of Reporter (Can the CAA contact you for further information?)
_____
_____

Please send as soon as possible to:     Canadian Avalanche Centre
                                        PO Box 2759, Revelstoke, British Columbia  V0E 2S0
                                        Fax: (250) 837-4624    Phone: (250) 837-2435

*Note:    This information will be used for public education and information. It may be summarized and published by the CAA. The reporter's name will not be published by the CAA.*

# Appendix B

# Glossary

**Symbols for Grain or Crystal Types**
See LaChapelle (1969) and McClung and Schaerer (1993) for information on crystal formation and metamorphism.

| | |
|---|---|
| + | precipitation particles (new snow forms) |
| / | decomposing and fragmented precipitation particles |
| • | rounded grains |
| □ | faceted crystals |
| ∧ | depth hoar |
| ○ | wet grains |
| ∨ | surface hoar |
| ■ | ice masses |
| ⋇ | crusts and surface deposits |
| ⊙∞ | melt-freeze crust |

Precipitation particles may be subclassified. Some subclasses used in this book are:

| | |
|---|---|
| ✳ | stellars and dendrites |
| ⟷ | needles |
| ⅄ | graupel (see rime) |
| ⌒ | irregular |

**Avalanche cycle -** A period of avalanches associated with a storm or warm weather. For snow storms, the cycle typically starts during the storm and ends a few days after the storm.

**Avalanche season (year)** - An avalanche year runs from October 1st to September 30th. For example, an accident that occurred on 22 December 1995 would be in the 1996 avalanche year.

**Avalanche transceiver** - An electronic device worn by travellers in avalanche terrain. In transmit mode, it constantly transmits a radio signal which is stronger at closer range. If someone with a transmitting transceiver is buried, the other members of the group can switch their transceivers into receive mode and follow a search pattern that locates the strongest signal. The person is then found by probing and shovelling.

**Bed surface** - The surface on which an avalanche runs. Not to be confused with failure plane (see failure plane).

**Bowl** - A slope that is shaped like half a bowl or funnel; becoming narrower towards the bottom.

**CARDA** - Canadian Avalanche Rescue Dog Association.

**Cornice** - An overhanging build-up of snow, usually on the lee side of ridges. Moderate or strong winds often create a vortex on the lee side and deposit wind-blown snow at the very top of the lee slope. Cornices generally form faster during periods of high humidity.

**Cross-loaded** - When wind blows across a cross-loaded slope, snow is picked up from windward ribs and outcrops and is deposited in lee pockets.

**Depth hoar** - An advanced, generally larger, form of faceted crystal (see facets). Depth hoar crystals are striated and, in later stages, often form hollow shapes. Cup-shaped crystals are a common form of depth hoar. This type of crystal can form at any level in the snowpack but is most commonly found at the base of shallow snowpacks following periods of cold weather.

**Failure plane** - The fracture that releases a slab avalanche spreads along a weak snowpack layer called the failure plane. The bed surface usually lies immediately below the failure plane. Failure planes are usually noticeably weaker than the bed surface.

**Facets** (also called faceted crystals or sometimes *sugar snow*) - In response to a sufficiently strong temperature gradient within the snowpack, grains grow flat faces by a process know as *kinetic growth* or simply *faceting*. Facets commonly form near the snow surface or where the snowpack is shallow during periods of cold weather.

**High-marking** (also called *high-pointing* or *hammer-heading*) - The activity in which snowmobilers drive up a steep slope, each trying to reach a higher point than the previous rider. When the sled slows at the top of the run, the rider turns down the slope.

**Melt-freeze crust** - A layer of snow that has been warmed until liquid water forms between the grains and then refrozen to form a relatively strong layer. Crusts sometimes form *the bed surface* for slab avalanches.

**Propagation** - The spreading of a fracture or crack. The shear fractures that spread along weak snow layers and release slab avalanches tend to propagate further under thicker, harder slabs than under thinner, softer slabs.

**Rime** - A deposit of ice from super-cooled water droplets. Rime can accumulate on the windward side of rocks, trees or structures, or on falling crystals of snow. When snow crystals cannot be recognised because of rime, the grains are called *graupel.*

**Rounded grains** (rounds) - Under sufficiently low *temperature gradients*, branched and angular crystals decompose into more rounded shapes called rounds. This dry-snow process involves the sublimation of ice from convex parts of grains into hollows. Rounding also tends to build bonds between grains (*sintering*). Consequently, layers of rounded grains are often stronger than layers of faceted grains of similar density.

**Rutschblock scores** - The rutschblock test is a slope stability test. A skier applies progressively increasing load to a 1.5 m by 2 m block of snow until a weak layer within the block fails (Föhn, 1987; CAA, 1995; Jamieson and Johnston, 1995b). See Table B.1.

*Table B.1 Rutschblock Loading Steps and Scores*

| Score | Loading step that produces a failure in a weak layer |
|---|---|
| RB 1 | The block slides during digging or cutting. |
| RB 2 | The skier approaches the block from above and gently steps down onto the upper part of the block (within 35 cm of the upper wall). |
| RB 3 | Without lifting the heels, the skier drops from straight leg to bent knee position, pushing downwards and compacting surface layers. |
| RB 4 | The skier jumps up and lands in the same compacted spot. |
| RB 5 | The skier jumps again onto the same compacted spot. |
| RB 6 | For hard or deep slabs, the skier removes their skis and jumps on the same spot. For soft slabs or thin slabs where jumping without skis might penetrate through the slab, the skier keeps the skis on, steps down another 35 cm, almost to mid-block, and pushes once and then jumps three times. |
| RB 7 | None of the loading steps produce a smooth slope-parallel failure. |

*Table B.2 Avalanche Size Classification*

| Size | Avalanche destructive potential | Typical path length |
|---|---|---|
| 1 | Relatively harmless to people. | 10 m |
| 2 | Could bury, injure, or kill a person. | 100 m |
| 3 | Could bury and destroy a car, damage a truck, destroy a small building, or break a few trees. | 1000 m |
| 4 | Could destroy a railway car, large truck, several buildings, or a forest area up to 4 hectares. | 2000 m |
| 5 | Largest snow avalanche known. Could destroy a village or a forest of 40 hectares. | 3000 m |

*Half sizes from 1.5 to 4.5 may be used for avalanches that are between two size classes.*

**Settlement** - The gradual compaction of snow layers under their own weight. The term is sometimes incorrectly used to describe a whumpf or propagating shear fracture.

**Slab** - One or more cohesive layers of snow that act as a unit.

**Sling rescue** - A rescue method in which a rescuer on a long line below a helicopter picks up a victim.

**Sluff** - A small avalanche usually made up of loose snow.

**Stepped down** - A slab avalanche is said to step down if the motion of the initial slab causes lower layers to slide, resulting in a second bed surface deeper in the snowpack. A step in the bed surface is usually visible.

**Storm snow** - The snow that falls during a period of continuous or almost continuous snowfall. Many operations consider a storm to be over after a day with less than 1 cm of snow.

**Sun crust** - The term sun crust is often used to refer to a melt-freeze crust that is more noticeable on sunny slopes than on shady slopes. However, the international definition is a thin, transparent layer (also called *firnspiegel*) caused by partial melting and refreezing of the

surface layer (Colbeck and others, 1990). Water vapour from just below the surface deposits as ice on the bottom of the sun crust.

**Surface hoar** - Crystals, often shaped like feathers, spikes or wedges, that grow upward from the snow surface when air just above the snow surface is cooled to the dew point. The winter equivalent of dew. Surface hoar grows most often when the wind is calm or light on cold, relatively clear nights. These crystals can also grow during the day on shady slopes. Once buried, layers of surface hoar are slow to gain strength, sometimes persisting for a month or more as potential failure planes for slab avalanches.

**Temperature gradient** - The temperature gradient is the change in temperature with depth in the snowpack. For example, if the temperature 20 cm below the surface is 3° warmer than the surface, then the temperature gradient in the top 20 cm averages 1.5° per 10 cm. Gradients greater than 1° per 10 cm are often associated with faceting of crystals and weakening of layers, whereas lower gradients are usually associated with rounding of grains and strengthening of layers. However, the transition between faceting and rounding also depends on factors other than the temperature gradient.

**Terrain trap** - A terrain feature that increases the consequences of getting caught in an avalanche. For example, gullies and crevasses increase the odds of a deep burial, and cliffs increase the odds of traumatic injuries.

**Whumpf** - The sound of a fracture propagating along a weak layer within the snowpack. Whumpfs are indicators of local instability. In terrain steep enough to avalanche, whumpfs usually result in slab avalanches.

**Wind-loaded** - Terrain on which the wind has deposited additional snow. Slopes on the lee sides of ridges are often wind-loaded.

**Wind-slab** - One or more stiff layers of wind-deposited snow. Wind slabs usually consist of snow crystals broken into small particles by the wind and packed together.

# Appendix C

# Avalanche Safety Books

**The ABC of Avalanche Safety**, second edition. E.R. LaChapelle. 1985. The Mountaineers, Seattle, WA. 112 p.

**Avalanche Accidents in Canada I, A Selection of Case Histories of Accidents, 1955 to 1976.** C.J. Stethem and P.A. Schaerer. 1979. National Research Council of Canada Publication 17292, 114 p.

**Avalanche Accidents in Canada II, A Selection of Case Histories of Accidents, 1943 to 1978.** C.J. Stethem and P.A. Schaerer. 1980. National Research Council of Canada Publication 18525, 75 p.

**Avalanche Accidents in Canada III, A Selection of Case Histories, 1978-1984.** P.A. Schaerer. 1987. National Research Council of Canada, Institute for Research in Construction, Publication 27950, 138 p.

**Avalanche Awareness, A Practical Guide to Safe Travel in Avalanche Terrain.** J. Moynier. 1993. Chockstone Press, 32 p.

**The Avalanche Book.** B.R. Armstrong and K. Williams. 1992. Fulcrum Publishing, Golden, Colorado, 240 p.

**The Avalanche Handbook.** D.M. McClung and P.A. Schaerer. The Mountaineers. 1993. Seattle, 271 p.

**Avalanche Safety for Skiers and Climbers** (second edition). Tony Daffern. 1993. Rocky Mountain Books, Calgary, Canada, 192 p.

**Avalanche Safety for Snowmobilers.** Bruce Jamieson. 1994. Snowline Technical Services, Calgary, 48 p.

**Backcountry Avalanche Awareness** (fourth edition). Bruce Jamieson. 1994. Snowline Technical Services, Calgary, 52 p.

**Snow Sense: A Guide to Evaluating Snow Avalanche Hazard.** Jill Fredston and Doug Fesler. 1994. Alaska Mountain Safety Center, Inc., Anchorage, Alaska, 116 p.

**The Snowy Torrents: Avalanche Accidents in the United States, 1910-1966.** Dale Gallagher (ed.) 1967. Alta Avalanche Study Center, USDA Forest Service, 144 p.

**The Snowy Torrents: Avalanche Accidents in the United States, 1967-1971.** K. Williams and B. Armstrong. 1975. USDA Forest Service General Technical Report RM-8, Fort Collins, Colorado, 190 p.

**The Snowy Torrents: Avalanche Accidents in the United States, 1972-79.** K. Williams and B. Armstrong. 1984. Teton Bookshop, Jackson, Wyoming, 221 p.

**The Snowy Torrents: Avalanche Accidents in the United States, 1980-86.** N. Logan and D. Atkins. 1996. Colorado Geological Survey Special Publication 39. Colorado Geological Survey, Denver Colorado, 265 p.

# Appendix D
# Canadian Avalanche Danger Scale (1996)

## AVALANCHE SAFETY BASICS

**Avalanches don't happen by accident** and most human involvement is a matter of **choice**, not chance. Most avalanche accidents are caused by **slab** avalanches which are triggered by the victim or by a member of the victim's party. However, **any** avalanche may cause injury or death and even small slides may be dangerous. Hence, always practise safe route finding skills, be aware of changing conditions, and carry avalanche rescue gear. Learn and apply avalanche terrain analysis and snow stability evaluation techniques to help minimize your risk. Remember that avalanche danger rating levels are only general guidelines. Distinctions between geographic areas, elevations, slope aspects and slope angles are approximate and transition zones between dangers exist.

### Canadian Avalanche Danger Descriptors

| Danger Level (& Color) | Avalanche Probability and Avalanche Trigger | Recommended Action in the Backcountry |
|---|---|---|
| …WHAT… | …WHY… | …WHAT TO DO… |
| **LOW** (green) | Natural avalanches very unlikely. Human-triggered avalanches **unlikely**. | Travel is generally safe. Normal caution advised. |
| **MODERATE** (yellow) | Natural avalanches unlikely. Human-triggered avalanches **possible**. | Use caution in steeper terrain on certain aspects (defined in accompanying statement). |
| **CONSIDERABLE** (orange) | Natural avalanches possible. Human-triggered avalanches **probable**. | Be increasingly cautious in steeper terrain. |
| **HIGH** (red) | Natural and human-triggered avalanches **likely**. | Travel in avalanche terrain is not recommended. |
| **EXTREME** (red with black border) | Widespread natural or human-triggered avalanches **certain**. | Travel in avalanche terrain should be avoided and travel confined to low angle terrain well away from avalanche path run-outs. |

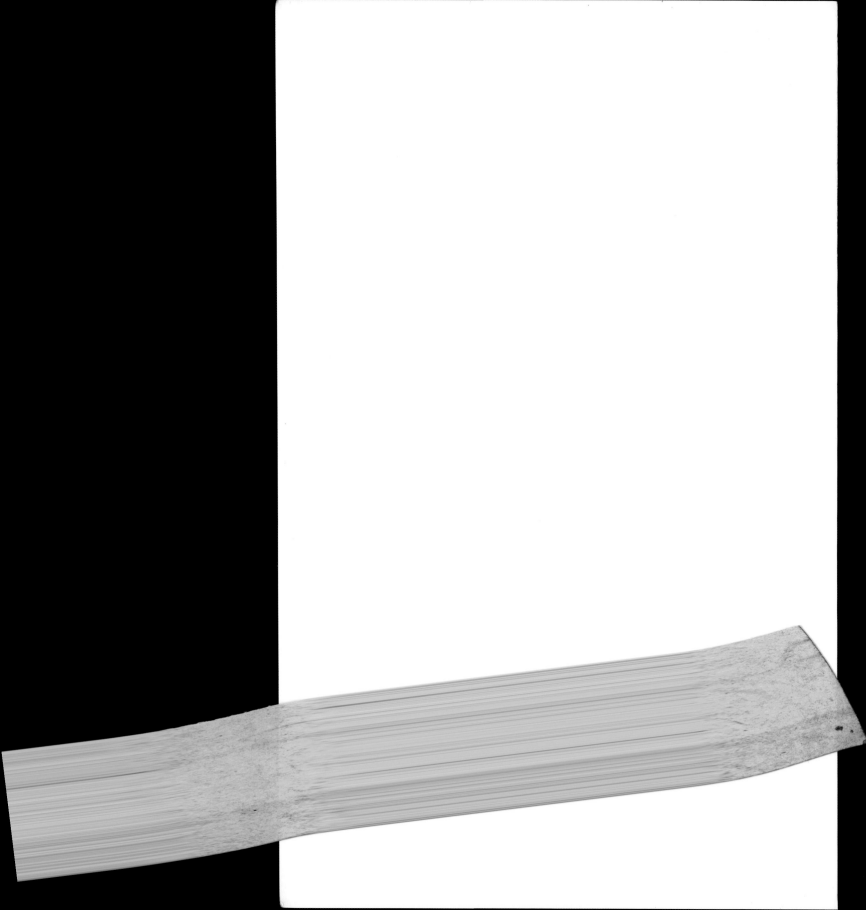

# About the Authors

**Bruce Jamieson** caught the mountain bug in 1974. Since then he has ski toured and climbed in North America and in the Andes of Peru and Bolivia. Before turning to avalanche research at the University of Calgary, he worked in avalanche control and forecasting from 1981 to 1986. His PhD in civil engineering focused on field tests of snow stability for avalanche forecasting. He is past president of the Canadian Avalanche Association and an active avalanche instructor. Presently, he splits his time between avalanche research, avalanche consulting and teaching. His booklets *Backcountry Avalanche Awareness* and *Avalanche Safety for Snowmobilers* are widely used for avalanche awareness courses in Canada.

**Torsten Geldsetzer** has travelled and worked in mountains all over the world. He is an avid ski tourer, freelance photographer and travel writer. He graduated from the University of Calgary with a degree in Physical Geography, specializing in climatology and glaciology. Following this, he worked at the Alfred Wegener Institute for Polar Research in Germany and also spent many summers working in the Canadian Arctic. Most recently, he has been the manager of the Canadian Avalanche Centre's snow stability information exchange and has also worked on numerous projects for the Canadian Avalanche Association. He now spends the winter involved in avalanche research and the summer as a hiking guide.